We invite you to explore, discover, be-
friend, listen to and learn from Mono Lake.
Get out and walk its beaches, float on its waters,
watch its birds and climb its volcanoes. Savor a sun-
rise, sunset and moonrise too. Then sit by a quiet shore
and ponder what our children will inherit. A
sterile sump? Or a living lake set in the midst
of natural splendor? The choice is ours.

Rebecca Shearin

Give me silence, water, hope
Give me struggle, iron, volcanoes
　　　　　　　　　—Pablo Neruda

MONO LAKE
Guidebook

by David Gaines and the Mono Lake Committee

illustrations by Rebecca Shearin, Keith Hansen and Joyce Jonte

photographs by Craig Aurness, Michael Beaucage, Michael Dressler, Liane Enkelis, Philip Hyde, Joseph R. Jehl, Jr., Stephen Johnson, Viki Lang, John S. Shelton, Galen Rowell, Jim Stroup, Brett Weston and others

maps by Sharon Johnson

Kutsavi  Books
Lee Vining

To Grace de Laet, Enid Larson, George Peyton, Jr. and Genny Smith, inspiring earth housekeepers and human beings, this guidebook is dedicated.

ISBN 0-939716-00-3/ Library of Congress Catalog No. 81-82402

Front cover photograph by Craig Aurness © National Geographic Society
Back cover photograph by Liane Enkelis
Title page drawing of a Sabine's Gull by Keith Hansen
Typesetting by Richard Ellington

The Mono Lake Committee is a non-profit citizens group devoted to protecting the scenic, wildlife, recreational and scientific values of Mono and other Great Basin Lakes. We invite your membership and support.

Mono Lake Committee/Kutsavi Books
P.O. Box 29
Lee Vining, CA 93541
Dealer inquiries welcomed.

Contents

Chapter 1　　DISCOVERING MONO LAKE　　1
A Self-guided Tour

Chapter 2　　THE LAKE AND ITS SETTING　　16
A country of Wonderful Contrasts; Saline and Alkaline; Strange
Water, Strange Tufa; Snowfields and Sagebrush; Fluctuating
Lake Levels; Geological History; During the Ice-ages; Volcanoes
and Volcanic Islands

Chapter 3　　THE LIVING SEA　　42
Few Species, Countless Individuals; Brine Shrimp vs. Algae;
Brine Flies, Midges and Monsters; Nesting Gulls and Plovers;
Travelers from Distant Shores; An Avian Gas Station; A
Troubled Future

Chapter 4　　HUMAN HISTORY: KUTSAVI-EATERS TO
WATER-SEEKERS　　58
Kuzedika Paiute; Mountain Men and Fortune Hunters; Writers
and Settlers; Robbing the Gulls; The Aqueduct Builders; Tapping
Into Mono

PHOTOGRAPHIC ESSAY　　67

Chapter 5　　TURNING PARADISE INTO ALKALI　　83
Owens Dry Lake; The Deadly Salt Build-up; Salt-stressed Birds;
Alkali Smog; What Will Be Lost?

Chapter 6　　COMMON-SENSE WATER USE CAN SAVE
MONO LAKE　　95
The Task Force Compromise; The Lesson of the California
Drought; A Wet Year/Dry Year Approach; Greed, Not Need;
Watershed Housekeeping

EPILOGUE by Gray Brechin　　105

WORDS OF THANKS　　106

SOURCES　　107

INDEX　　112

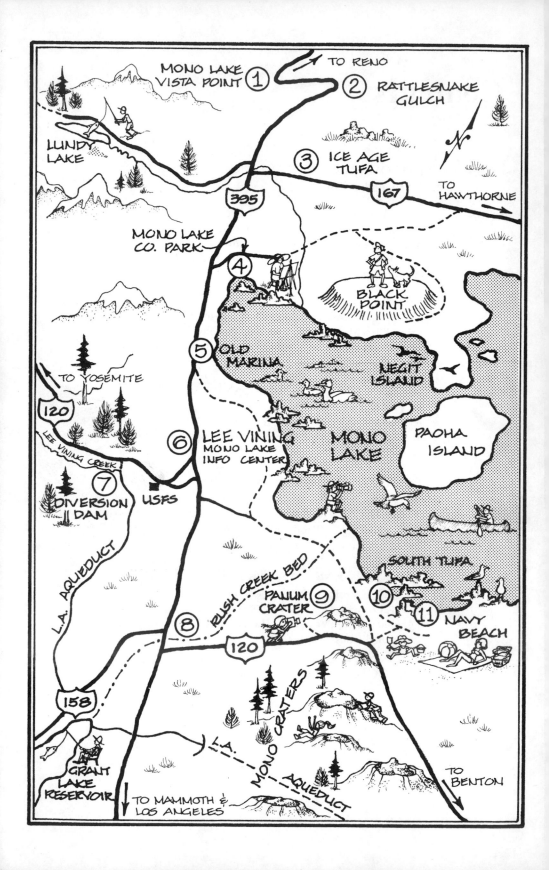

1

Discovering Mono Lake a self-guided tour

Rebecca Shearin

Mono Lake needs new friends and will not begrudge more foot-prints on its shores, provided you walk lightly. This self-guided tour will get you oriented. Along the way you will learn of Mono's history, geology, wildlife and future—topics covered in depth in the chapters that follow.

Allow at least half a day to complete the tour. Use the map on the opposite page to navigate. If time is limited, visit the South Tufa Grove (Stop 10) or the Mono Lake County Park (Stop 4). Bring a hat and sunscreen to temper the sun and glare. Wear walking shoes that don't mind getting wet. Plan on a swim in Mono's buoyant water and a picnic among its tufa spires.

Stop 1: MONO LAKE VISTA POINT – PANORAMIC VIEW OF THE WATERSHED

The tour begins at the Mono Lake Vista Point along Highway 395 twelve miles north of Lee Vining and just south of Conway Summit. More than one thousand feet below, Mono Lake lies cradled by mountains and volcanos. The sketch identifies the most prominent peaks and landmarks:

- The White Mountains 50 miles to the southeast, whose summit, White Mountain Peak (14,246'), is only 250 feet lower than Mt. Whitney.

A WARNING ON SIDE-ROADS

The side-roads traveled in this tour are passable to ordinary passenger cars. Many others are not. Unless you are equipped with 4-wheel drive, stay on graded, well-traveled routes and do not pull off onto shoulders to turn around or park. It is easy to get stuck in the soft sand.

- Glass Mountain (11,123′), a volcano that erupted about 900,000 years ago.
- The Mono Craters, a young chain of volcanoes that we will visit later in this tour.
- The steep, glacier-sculpted peaks of the central Sierra Nevada looming 40 miles to the south (Mt. Whitney is 65 miles farther south).

You are at the western edge of the Great Basin, an arid, mountainous region that stretches across Nevada and Utah to the Rockies. Throughout the Great Basin, streams do not drain to the ocean. Rather they vanish in sandy valleys or collect in inland seas, of which Great Salt, Pyramid and Mono Lakes are the best known.

As you can see, Mono lies in a deep depression. Water reaches the lake from snow-fed Sierran streams, but leaves only through evaporation into the atmosphere.

At the close of the Ice Ages, when glaciers melted up Sierran canyons, Mono Lake filled its basin to the brim and even overflowed into Owens, Panamint and ultimately Death Valleys. An inland sea reached for miles into the Nevadan desert. As recently as 13,000 years ago, waves lapped the bottom of the slope on which you stand.

Before departing, notice the "bathtub-ring" of white alkali around Mono's shores. It marks the lake's shrinkage, not over millenia or even centuries, but during the last decade. Mono Lake is drying up, not due to natural causes, but because of the thirst of a distant metropolis. Looking towards black Negit Island, you can see

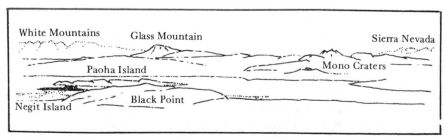

Looking south from the Mono Lake Vista Point near Conway Summit.

RECREATION AT THE LAKE

Swimming

Swimming in Mono Lake is a delightfully buoyant experience, for you cannot sink in the dense water. Old-timers claim a soak cures almost anything. But keep the water out of eyes and cuts—it stings! After a float, rinse the salts off your skin with fresh water. The south shore, especially Navy Beach, has the best swimming spots.

Canoeing and Boating

Beware of the weather! Sudden winds can capsize even sturdy craft. People have drowned as recently as 1978.

With caution and good sense, boating can be perfectly safe. Unless you are sure of the weather (tricky!), stay close to shore. Always carry life-jackets and let someone know where you are going and when you will return. Do not attempt to cross the lake after mid-morning or when even a light breeze is blowing. You'll have to portage your canoe, kayak, raft, sailboat or cabin cruiser to the lakeshore. Best points to embark are Navy Beach and South Tufa.

Visiting the Islands

From March through August, please leave the islands to the birds. Human disturbance, however well-intentioned, wreaks havoc and may even cause nests and young to be abandoned.

If you decide to visit the islands when the birds are elsewhere, go prepared. Always carry sleeping bags, warm clothes and extra food and water, for you may be marooned by inclement weather. If a storm blows in, stay put. In 1978 six people lost their lives when they tried to return from Paoha against 50 mile-per-hour winds and six-foot waves.

Birdwatching

April through October are the birdiest months. Northbound shore-birds, grebes and ducks arrive in early spring, as do nesting Spotted Sandpipers, American Avocets, Common Snipe, Snowy Plovers and California Gulls. The southward migration begins in July and continues through October, bringing thousands of Wilson's and Northern Phalaropes and hundreds of thousands of Eared Grebes. Among the less common but regular visitors are Sanderlings, Baird's, Solitary and Pectoral Sandpipers, Red Knots and Ruddy Turnstones. In addition Golden Plovers, Wandering Tattlers, Sabine's Gulls and three species of Jaeger have all reached the lake on several occasions. Birdwatching is best near the deltas of freshwater streams and springs, as at Mono Lake County Park and South Tufa.

the landbridge that was uncovered in 1979, allowing coyotes to invade the gull rookeries. If the wind is blowing, white clouds of dust will be billowing off the exposed lakebottom.

One final point. Don't believe the highway department's interpretive sign. It describes Mono Lake as a "dead sea," when in fact it is teeming with life.*

Stop 2: RATTLESNAKE GULCH – THE MONOVILLE GOLD RUSH

From the Mono Lake Vista Point, Highway 395 descends among picturesque granite outcroppings. If time allows, pull off the highway about a mile down the road. There is a large turnout on the right just before the hairpin turn. Cross the highway and walk east along the dirt road about one-half mile into Rattlesnake Gulch, the site of Mono County's first gold strike (don't worry—rattlesnakes are as scarce as gold, and as afraid of you as you are of them). In 1859 miners founded Monoville, Mono's first town. Not a trace remains, for everything, lumber and all, was hauled to another strike, Aurora, three years later. Aurora, in turn, was eclipsed in the 1870s by the biggest and wildest camp of them all—Bodie.**

Stop 3: HIGHWAY 167 – ICE-AGE TUFA

From Rattlesnake Gulch, follow Highway 395 a few miles south to the junction with Highway 167, the road to Hawthorne. Turn left, drive 1.3 miles east, then park just off the road on the right (there is ample space, but beware of soft sand).

Look among the sagebrush for jumbles of gray-colored rocks covered with dull orange lichens. The rocks are composed of small lance- and spear-shaped crystals, called *thinolite,* fitted together in complex yet delicate latticeworks. Their overall shapes are bulbous in outline, as if they somehow bubbled out of the earth. These unusual rocks are ancient tufa towers which grew beneath the waters of ice-age Mono Lake over 13,000 years ago. We will learn more about tufa at our next stop.

The tufa are not the only evidence that Mono's waters have covered this spot. On the low hills to the north and northeast, the waves of the ice-age lake incised horizontal beach terraces. They are easiest to see in the early morning and late afternoon, when shadows highlight the lay of the land.

---

*The sign also maligns Chief Tenaya, who only "massacred" prospectors after his own people, including women and children, were slaughtered by gold-miners.

**Now a State Historical Park, Bodie may be reached by a paved road that branches east off Highway 395 six miles north of Conway Summit.

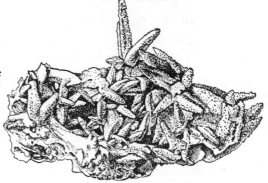

Mono's ice-age tufa (Stop 3) are adorned with delicate thinolite crystals.[5]

Before departing, pick a sprig of gray-green foliage from a sage-brush. Crush a leaf and inhale its spicy fragrance, the perfume of the Great Basin.

If time allows, drive another few miles east on Highway 167 and savor the spaciousness and solitude. On your return to Highway 395, note the rise just before the junction. It demarcates an ice-age beach terrace.

Stop 4: MONO LAKE COUNTY PARK — NORTH SHORE TUFA

From the junction of Highways 395 and 167, drive south 2.5 miles on Highway 395, then turn left on Cemetery Road to the Mono Lake County Park. The turnoff is well-marked. Before proceeding to the park itself, pause to enjoy the view of Black Point, Negit and Paoha Islands, the White Mountains, Glass Mountain and the Mono Craters.

The park itself, situated along a small stream and shaded by cottonwoods, is an idyllic picnic spot. The site was once a pioneer homestead (note the old, still fruitful apple trees north of Cemetery Road). Like so many farms in the Mono Basin, it was purchased by the Los Angeles Department of Water and Power in the 1930s. Since 1973, the City has leased the land to Mono County for use as a park.

Walk towards the lake from the restroom building. The way is

Looking east from the junction of Highway 395 and Cemetery Road.

DON'T MOLEST THE TUFA

Submerged in Mono's waters, the tufa were protected from deface-
ment and vandalism. Exposed on its shores they are climbed on, shot at,
driven over and carried off as souvenirs. Snow, rain and wind, of course,
will gradually erode them anyway. But natural weathering will not only be
slow, it will sculpt the tufa into new, intriguing shapes (as it has the tufa
formed in the ice-age lake). So take only pictures . . . and share this ethic
with others.

---

soggy in spots, so wear waterproof boots or resign yourself to wet
shoes and socks (it's well worth it). Stay to the left of the small
creek and follow the path through boggy meadows (bright with wild
iris in June) to the first tufa formations.

The tufa towers are built by freshwater springs as they well up
through Mono's brine. Calcium in the freshwater combines with carbonates in the lake, forming tufa, which is chemically identical to
limestone. Over time the deposits accumulate and are sculpted by
currents and waves. As the lake recedes, they are marooned along
its shores.

You can follow the stream almost to the lakeshore. Breathe the
salty air and listen to the lap of the waves and the cries of the gulls.
You are at a seashore in the heart of the continent.

If time allows, explore the shores to the east. Springs, meadows
and tufa spires await your discovery.

HALF-DAY HIKE: BLACK POINT – AN UNDERWATER VOLCANO

To the east of Mono Lake County Park, a hill of black cinders
dominates the skyline. It is Black Point, a volcano that erupted beneath the waters of ice-age Mono Lake 13,800 years ago. Deep,
narrow fissures furrow its summit.

Allow half a day to hike Black Point. There is no trail, but the
ascent is gentle. It is easiest to start from the dirt road on its eastern
flank (see map facing p. 1). Search for the fissures near the point's
southwestern rim.

Stop 5: MONO LAKE MARINA SITE –
WEST SHORE AND ISLANDS

From the County Park, return to Highway 395 and turn left
past the Mono Inn. Built by the Wallis D. McPherson family in 1922,
the inn was a lively lakeside resort during the 1930s and 1940s. A
large sign welcomed travelers to "the lake that made Mark Twain

Excursions to Mono's islands were popular during the 1930s and 1940s. Sightseers visited Negit's gull rookery and Paoha's crater lakelets (now dry), and swam in the thermally heated water of Paoha's hot springs cove.

famous." A voyage to the islands was de rigueur. The excursion boat *Venita* resides in the pasture behind and to the south of the inn, where it was wrecked by a violent storm in 1952. The inn has changed ownership and is now a restaurant.

About one mile south of the Mono Inn you pass the brine shrimp processing plant operated by Jungle Labs. Approximately 250 tons of shrimp (over 20 billion individuals) are harvested each summer— an infinitesimal fraction of the lake's population![1] The tiny shrimp, which are less than one-half inch in length, are captured in fine mesh nets anchored around underwater springs. The upwelling water sweeps the shrimp into the nets. Brought in by boat, they are packaged and marketed as fish food.

A little further south, around the next bend on Highway 395, the Tioga Lodge is shaded by cottonwoods. Years ago it was a fashionable resort renowned for elegant flower gardens. In 1956 a flash flood roared down the canyon behind the lodge and swept buildings and cars into the lake. It is being renovated by new owners.

One mile beyond Tioga Lodge, just before the highway climbs to Lee Vining, turn left on the short, unmarked paved road that leads to the site of the Mono Lake Marina. Back in the 1950s and 1960s this was a popular swimming beach, picnic spot and boat launch. In those days Mono's waters extended nearly to the highway. Now a broad strip of white, alkali-encrusted muck separates the weathered docks from what is left of the lake.

Looking east across Mono's waters, the black lava of Negit Island contrasts with Paoha Island's tawny bluffs. Within the last thousand years both islands rose from the lake amidst fiery clouds of

Liane Enkelis

Nets laden with brine shrimp are
hauled aboard a raft near Mono's
northwest shore. The shrimp are
marketed as fish food.

steam and ash.

Negit and Paoha were named by one of America's most brilliant
geologists, Israel C. Russell. In 1877 he gave up a professorship to
explore the Great Basin, eventually spending three years in the Mono
Basin. Russell saw grandeur where others saw desolation, and forged
a literary style equal to that vision. His *Quaternary History of the
Mono Valley* blends science with prose so vivid and powerful that
residents at the time paid to reprint the study as an enticement to
tourists.

The naming of the islands reflects Russell's romanticism. "It was
suggested," he wrote, "that the differences in color might be used,
but the writer preferred to record some of the poetic words from the
language of the aboriginal inhabitants of the valley." "Negit," appro-
priately, is a Paiute word for "gull."* "Paoha" are "diminutive spirits, having long, wavy hair, that are sometimes seen in the vapor
wreaths ascending from hot springs," such as those on the white
island.[2]

Paoha has seen its share of homesteaders. Back in 1884 a French-
man named Fisher tried hatching chickens on the island's sulfurous
steam vents.[3] In the 1910s, before constructing Mono Inn, the Mc-
Phersons raised goats, rabbits and vegetables on its lonely shores. In

---

*Russell translates "Negit" as "blue-winged goose," but geese are unknown on the island;
the word undoubtedly means "gull."

the 1940s a sanitarium came and went. Only the wind dwells there
today.

Stop 6: LEE VINING-MONO LAKE INFORMATION CENTER

From the Mono Lake Marina, continue south on Highway 395.
As you ascend the hill to Lee Vining, watch for weathered tufa towers
on the slopes to your right.

The town of Lee Vining sits on a delta formed during the last ice
age. At that time Mono Lake stood as high or higher than the town.
Lee Vining Creek swept tons of glacier-quarried rock and gravel down
its canyon, building the delta out into the ice-age lake.

While in Lee Vining, stop at the Mono Lake Information Center
at the corner of Highway 395 and Third Street. The exhibits will en-
hance your appreciation and enjoyment of the lake. The staff will be
happy to answer questions and help you plan your explorations. The
center, operated by the non-profit Mono Lake Committee, is open
to the public free of charge.

Food, film, gas, accommodations and other visitor services are
readily available in Lee Vining. The town name commemorates the
prospector Leroy Vining, who became Mono's first white settler in
1853. In the early 1860s he operated a sawmill in the canyon that
likewise bears his name, hauling lumber to the boom town of Aurora.
He met an untimely end, accidentally shooting and killing himself
with his own revolver in an Aurora saloon.

Frasher's Photography

The McPherson homestead on Paoha Island, ca. 1930, looking west toward the
Sierra Nevada. From 1917 until 1922 the McPhersons raised goats, rabbits and
vegetables on the island's lonely shores. Fire has destroyed the house and barn.
In 1977, the property was purchased by Los Angeles.

Michael Dressler

The Lee Vining diversion dam and intake. At this point, water from Lee Vining Creek is shunted into the Los Angeles Aqueduct.

Stop 7: LEE VINING CANYON –
DIVERSION DAM AND GLACIAL EROSION

Continue south on Highway 395 about one mile beyond Lee Vining, then turn right on Highway 120 west toward Tioga Pass and Yosemite. About two miles up the canyon and 0.7 mile beyond the Forest Service Ranger Station, turn left on a graded, unmarked dirt road that leads across a meadow to the Lee Vining Diversion Dam.

At this point Lee Vining Creek, Mono Lake's second largest tributary stream, is diverted into the Los Angeles Aqueduct. The intake is at the far end of the small, concrete dam. Large, buried conduits transport the water to Grant Lake Reservoir. These facilities, built in the 1930s, are the northernmost link in the aqueduct system.

If you had stood on this spot 13,000 years ago, you would have been crushed under 500 feet of glacial ice. Notice the shape of the canyon. Had it been eroded by water alone, it would be V-shaped in cross-section. But, like Yosemite Valley, it is U-shaped. Advancing glaciers scoured out the wide, level canyon floor and left the high, parallel ridges, called lateral moraines, on either side.

On your return to Highway 395, pause to enjoy the view from the vista point below the ranger station.

Stop 8: RUSH CREEK – DYING OF THIRST

After you reach Highway 395, turn right and drive five miles south to the junction with Highway 120 east, the road to Benton. On the way, notice the fresh-looking, horizontal swath cut high on the hillside to your right. This marks the route of the Los Angeles Aqueduct as it transports Lee Vining Creek water to Grant Lake, a holding reservoir on Rush Creek. On the way it also collects water from Parker and Walker Creeks. From Grant Lake Reservoir, the diverted water flows through a tunnel under the Mono Craters, into the Owens River and on to Los Angeles (maps 6 and 7, pp. 32–33).

Just south of the June Lake Loop turnoff and before the junction with Highway 120 east, Highway 395 dips and crosses Rush Creek, once Mono Lake's largest tributary stream. Stumps and snags are all that remain of the aspens and pines that once lined its banks. A trout stream has become a wash.

Mono Lake is likewise dying of thirst. Diversions are now taking 80 percent of the water from its tributary streams. As a result, the lake is dropping an average of 18 inches each year. Since diversions began, it has fallen 45 feet, its volume has been halved, its salinity has doubled and over 20 square miles of lakebottom have been laid bare to the sun and wind.

Stop 9: PANUM CRATER — VOLCANIC FIREWORKS

From Highway 395 turn left onto Highway 120 east. The first mile affords dramatic views of the Mono Craters. Twenty volcanic domes rise 2,600 feet above the surrounding plains. Were they not dwarfed by the Sierra Nevada they would be much better known, not only for their height, but for their symmetrical domes and jagged lava

Ca. 1920: Lower Rush Creek is the finest Brown Trout stream in the eastern Sierra.

courtesy of Enid Larson

1981: Lower Rush Creek is a bone dry wash, its water diverted into the Los Angeles Aqueduct.

Viki Lang

Adapted from Russell

Looking north from Highway 120 toward Panum Crater and Mono Lake.

flows. They have erupted in recent centuries and may do so again in our lifetimes.

After traveling 3.2 miles east on Highway 120, turn left onto the unmarked dirt road that leads to Panum Crater. Go slow, as the road is easy to miss. Walk or drive 0.7 mile north, then park in the open area on your right. This is also the best place to turn around.

A short, easy walk leads to the top of Panum Crater's circular pumice ring. The view is expansive. To the west rise the precipitous Sierra Nevada, uplifted by three and one-half million years of faulting. Notice the extensive glacial moraines at the mouths of Sierran canyons.

Panum's pumice ring was formed by explosive eruptions only 640 years ago. Ash was blown as far away as Kings Canyon National

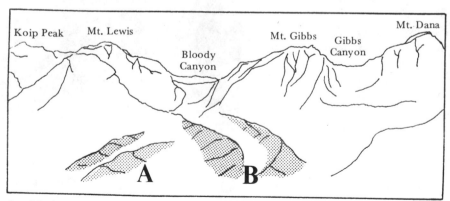

Looking west from Panum Crater toward the Sierra Nevada. The two pairs of lateral glacial moraines at the mouth of Bloody Canyon are evidence of two glacial advances. After depositing moraines A, the glacier retreated up the canyon. Thousands of years later, a glacier returned. But instead of following the path of its predecessor, it crossed the older moraines and veered slightly north, leaving moraines B.

Ian Tait

Mono brine shrimp.

Park. Following the formation of the ring, thick, pasty lava rose out of the volcano's throat like toothpaste from a tube, plugging its vent. This jagged plug dome is largely composed of obsidian (volcanic glass), which forms when lava cools rapidly. Obsidian was fashioned into arrowheads by the region's Indian inhabitants.

Stop 10: SOUTH TUFA – THE LAKE AND ITS WILDLIFE

Return to Highway 120, turn left and follow the road east as it rises to a saddle, then descends and swings to the right. The saddle offers another sweeping view of Mono Lake and its watershed. At the bottom of the hill, six miles east of Highway 395, a graded dirt road takes off to the left toward Mono's south shore. A small sign marks the turnoff. Almost immediately the road forks, the right branch leading to Navy Beach and the left to South Tufa. Proceed to South Tufa first; then, time permitting, retrace your route and visit Navy Beach.

Drive one mile down the left fork to the parking area. The Bureau of Land Management has closed the South Tufa Grove to vehicles in order to protect its tufa spires. A short walk through grassy meadows leads to Mono's shore. The grasses are watered by the same springs that gave birth to tufa when the lake was higher.

Feel the water. It's slick and slippery. Moisten a finger and touch it to your tongue. The water is salty, but bitter too. That salty taste is sodium chloride, ordinary table salt. The bitterness derives from carbonates (baking soda) and other substances. Salts and minerals washed into the lake are concentrated as pure water evaporates. Over millenia, Mono has become three times as salty and 80 times as alkaline as the ocean.

Notice the oily upwellings just offshore. Many visitors suppose that oil is seeping from the lakebottom. In fact, the "oily substance" is ordinary fresh water rising through Mono's denser brine. You can prove it for yourself by pouring fresh water into the lake. The up-wellings mark the location of lakebottom springs.

If it is summertime, the water will be clear and filled with danc-ing brine shrimp. They feed on microscopic algae (green plants) too small to be seen by the naked eye. In September, after laying eggs that hatch the following spring, the adults die. Without shrimp to eat them, the algae grow so rapidly the lake turns green.

Harmless little brine flies abound along the lakeshore. The im-mature stages (larvae and pupae) which develop in the lake were har-vested by Mono Basin's native people, the *Kuzedika Paiute* or *fly-pupae eaters*. The Indian word *Mono* means *fly people* and *brine fly*, not in the Paiute language, but in that of their Yokut neighbors.[4] The Yokut, who dwelt in the Yosemite region, considered the flies a delicacy.

From May through October, uncountable numbers of birds gather to feast on the shrimp and flies. Mono's surface is peppered with grebes, gulls, shorebirds and ducks. The abundance of birds is related to the absence of fish, which cannot survive in the salty lake. Without fish competing for shrimp and flies, the birds enjoy an inex-haustible food supply.

In years to come, however, birds may starve along Mono's shores. As the lake shrinks, its salts become ever more concentrated. Brine shrimp, brine flies and algae can thrive in salty water, but not in salty, salty, salty water. Unless diversions are curtailed, increasing salinity will poison Mono's inhabitants.

Take a moment to envision a shrunken, sterile Mono Lake. From where you now stand, it would be mud-slogging miles to the shore. Hardly a bird would greet you; not a shrimp would animate the life-less water. Instead of clouds of birds there would be clouds of dust.

This doesn't have to happen. California has more than adequate water for people, agriculture and places like Mono Lake, if only we use existing supplies wisely.

For the moment, however, Mono's south shore retains much of

its grandeur. Take an hour or more to stroll along the lakeshore. Rippled tufa pavements glisten with crystals; spires reach out of their watery reflections; warm springs tell of volcanic fires simmering below.

Stop 11: NAVY BEACH — SAND TUFA

To reach Navy Beach, continue walking east 1.5 miles beyond South Tufa, or drive back to the fork near Highway 120 and turn left. About one mile from the fork, the road to Navy Beach reaches a T-intersection. From here it is an easy 200-yard walk to the broad beach of pumice sand. In the 1960s the Navy tested explosives just offshore.

Along the road to the left are fragile, waist-high sand tufa that formed in the sediments beneath Mono's waters. Since the lake's retreat, winds have stripped the sand away, exposing the tufa.

From Navy Beach you can hike to springs, tufa groves and beaches as wonderful as those you have already seen. But we're not going to tell you which way to head. As Aldo Leopold said, "Of what avail are forty freedoms without a blank spot on the map?" Wherever you venture, you will be rewarded.

Dennis Studer

2

The Lake and its Setting

A COUNTRY OF WONDERFUL CONTRASTS

If America were divided into geographic regions based on geology, climate, plants and animals, the Mono Lake watershed would straddle a great natural boundary. To the west the lofty Sierra Nevada wrings the moisture from Pacific storms, watering meadows and forests, lakes and streams. To the east an immense expanse of almost unrelieved aridity reaches across Nevada to Great Salt Lake and the Wasatch Mountains of Utah.

The parched region between the Sierra and the Wasatch was named the *Great Basin* by John C. Fremont in 1844, who realized its streams came to rest in the desert (Map 2, p. 27). Early explorers had embroidered fact and hearsay into imaginary rivers that were said to flow westwards through the Sierra to the Pacific. The myths persisted until Fremont traced the basin's streams into dessicated valleys, alkali-encrusted playas and saline lakes without outlets.[1]

The term Great Basin is misleading, for the region is corrugated into more than 100 independent basins separated by steep mountains. Range after parallel range rise along north-south axes to elevations of 9,000 to 12,000 feet. Between lie deep troughs filled with sediment— long, level valleys clothed in sagebrush, greasewood and shadscale.

Mono Lake's watershed, the Mono Basin, is an exception. It is not a narrow trough between mountain ranges but rather a shallow,

16

MONO LAKE'S VITAL STATISTICS[3]

	SURFACE ELEVATION			
	7,180' highstand of ice-age lake	6,410' estimated level no diversions	6,373' 1981 level	6,323' projected level present diversions
SIZE (including islands)				
SURFACE AREA	345 sq. miles	86 sq. miles	61 sq. miles	35 sq. miles
VOLUME*	~118,000,000 AF	4,050,000 AF	2,300,000 AF	780,000 AF
AVERAGE DEPTH	?	~75 feet	~50 feet	?
MAXIMUM DEPTH	956 feet	186 feet	150 feet	99 feet
LENGTH OF				
SHORELINE	~130 miles	~60 miles	~35 miles	~25 miles
SALINITY†	?	5.2%	9.5%	~27%
NEGIT ISLAND				
SURFACE AREA	—	~150 acres	no longer island	no longer island
ELEVATION ABOVE LAKE	—	180 feet	—	—
PAOHA ISLAND				
SURFACE AREA	—	~1,500 acres	—	no longer island
ELEVATION ABOVE LAKE	—	286 feet	—	—

*AF = acre-foot
†percent dissolved solids by weight

bathtub-shaped depression cupped by the lofty Sierra Nevada on its west and rolling volcanic uplands on its north, east and south (Map 1). Roughly 25 miles wide, it is a relatively small drainage. Yet it is a land of high relief and striking contrasts. Huddled between the snowy Sierra and the parched Great Basin, it partakes of both worlds. From 13,000 feet perennial snowfields and small glaciers look down on sagebrush desert. On the west Sierran streams crash down deep wooded canyons. To the east cobbled washes, dry most of the year, course through arid scrub-covered hills. To the south a chain of young, explosive volcanoes, the Mono Craters, rise 2,500 feet above a pumice-strewn plain. "A country of wonderful contrasts," wrote John Muir over a century ago, "hot deserts bordered by snow-laden mountains, cinders and ashes scattered on glacier-polished pavement, frost and fire working together in the making of beauty."[2]

The blue expanse of Mono Lake, with its black and white volcanic islands, occupies the bottom of the Mono Basin bathtub. It lies at an elevation of 6,373 feet, over a mile below the Sierran peaks that spawn its tributary streams. Twice the size of San Francisco, it stretches 13 miles east-west by eight miles north-south. It is shallow, especially to the east where its waters lap a gently sloping plain. To

Map 1. This relief map of Mono Lake, drawn by Willard D. Johnson in 1883, is a masterpiece of nineteenth century topography. Underwater contours have been added.[27]

the west it is deeper, reaching a maximum depth of 150 feet south of Paoha Island. Although its average depth is only 50 feet, no other natural lake entirely within California holds a greater volume of water.* And such strange water too![3]

SALINE AND ALKALINE

Mono Lake's unusual chemistry has fascinated visitors as well as scientists since the nineteenth century. Imagine, after many days of travel through sagebrush desert, coming upon an azure lake cradled by snow-clad mountains and fed by streams of the greatest purity, only to find its water, as an old miner put it, "quite as strong as a whisky cocktail in a country hotel."[4] "Its sluggish waters," wrote Mark Twain, "are so strong with alkali that if you only dip the most hopelessly soiled garment into them once or twice, and wring it out, it will be found as clean as if it had been through the ablest of washer-woman's hands." How has pure snowmelt been transformed into a bitter brine of dissolved carbonates, sulfates, chlorides and other minerals?

The streams feeding Mono Lake, although fresh and drinkable,

---

*Lake Tahoe is larger, but lies partially in Nevada; Clear Lake has a greater surface area, but holds less water.

pick up trace amounts of salts and minerals as they flow over rocks and soil. Because the lake has no outlet, these substances collect in its water, where they are concentrated as fresh water evaporates. The process of evaporative concentration is easily demonstrated by boiling a pot of salted water. As fresh water boils away, that remaining in the pot becomes increasingly saline. Eventually a white layer of precipitated salts analagous to that along the shores of present-day Mono Lake is all that is left in the bottom of the pot.

The ocean is salty for exactly the same reason. So are many other landlocked inland seas, called *terminal lakes,* scattered about the arid parts of the earth. The chemistry of a particular terminal lake is a function of the length of time salts and minerals have been accumulating in its water, the types of rock weathering in its watershed and chemical reactions in the lake itself. No two are exactly alike, and some, like Mono, are exceedingly unusual.[5]

For example, compare Mono's salinity, alkalinity and chemical composition with those of Lake Tahoe, the ocean and Great Salt Lake. Salinity is a measure of the total dissolved solids in a given volume of water. At present Mono holds about 340 million tons of dissolved salts—almost a pound per gallon of lakewater (95 grams per liter). This makes it 10,000 times saltier than Lake Tahoe, almost three times saltier than seawater, slightly less salty than Great Salt Lake's

MONO LAKE'S WATER CHEMISTRY COMPARED TO TAHOE, THE OCEAN AND GREAT SALT LAKE
(salinity in % dissolved solids by weight; solutes in grams/liter)[6]

	salinity	chlorides	carbonates, bicarbonates	sulfates	pH
Mono Lake — 6,410' *estimated level, no diversions*	5.2%	11 g/l	18 g/l	6 g/l	10
Mono Lake — 6,373' *1981 elevation*	9.5%	19.8 g/l	32.7 g/l	10.9 g/l	10
Mono Lake — 6,223' *projected level, present diversions*	27%	56 g/l	93 g/l	31 g/l	10
Lake Tahoe	0.001%	—	—	—	7.6
Ocean	3.5%	19.0 g/l	—	2.5 g/l	8.1
Great Salt Lake — s. arm	12%	67 g/l	—	9 g/l	8.0
Great Salt Lake — n. arm	34%	191 g/l	—	23 g/l	8.0

Additional substances in Mono Lake (1981): potassium (1.6 g/l), boron (0.5 g/l)

---

*In 1959, a railroad causeway was completed across Great Salt Lake, dividing it into north and south arms. Freshwater inflow dilutes the south arm, keeping it less saline.

Rebecca Shearin

Figure 1. Salinity measures total dissolved solids in a given volume of water—not just sodium chloride (table salt), but carbonates, sulfates and other substances as well. Mono Lake's present salinity is almost three times that of seawater and 10,000 times that of Lake Tahoe, but less than one-third that of the north arm of Great Salt Lake. This is not the whole story, for Mono's chemical composition differs radically from that of the ocean, Great Salt and most other saline lakes (see text). If water diversions continue, Mono will become about as salty as Salt Lake's biologically depauperate north arm.[6]

south arm, and about one-third as salty as Great Salt's north arm (Figure 1).*[6]

In terms of chemical composition, Mono differs radically from Great Salt and most other saline lakes. Three substances dominate its waters: (1) chlorides, mostly sodium chloride (NaCl), ordinary table salt, (2) carbonates and bicarbonates, mostly sodium carbonate (Na_2CO_3), a relative of baking soda, and (3) sulfates, mostly sodium sulfate (Na_2SO_4). Seawater, by comparison, is richer in chloride but poorer in sulfate and carbonate. So is Great Salt Lake, whose waters hold up to 10 times more chloride, but virtually no carbonate. Mono is also exceptionally rich in borate and potassium. These peculiarities largely determine what can and cannot live in the lake, as we shall learn in Chapter 3.

Because of Mono's high carbonate concentrations, the lake is alkaline as well as salty. Alkalinity and acidity are measured on the pH scale of 0 to 14. Pure water, with a pH of 7, is neutral. Each whole number higher marks a tenfold increase in alkalinity, each number lower a tenfold increase in acidity. Hence Mono Lake, at a pH close to 10, is about 80 times more alkaline than seawater, which has a *p*H of 8.1. It is 100 times as alkaline as Great Salt Lake (*p*H about 8) and about 250 times as alkaline as Lake Tahoe (*p*H about 7.6). Alkalinity imparts a slippery feel and bitter taste to the water, as well as those cleansing qualities praised by Twain.

Mono, in sum, is a salty, soda, sulfurous lake. Or, as scientists would say, a chloro-carbonate-sulfate or *triple water* lake. To find a similar body of water you would have to journey half way around the earth to the rift valley of equatorial Africa. Even in that distant land, a chemical twin does not exist.

STRANGE WATER, STRANGE TUFA

Mono is no ordinary lake. Its dramatic setting, saline, alkaline water and vast flocks of birds set it apart from any place else on earth. So do the strange but delicate mineral formations, called *tufa,* that grace its shores.

These improbable sculptures, which seem to belong to a distant planet, have been variously described as "giant towers of cemented cauliflower," "white columns and elaborate facades, like those of the ruined temples of Greece," and "science-fiction art . . . the cities of some intelligent and artistic extraterrestrial termite."[7] Their artistry is unrivalled. In other alkaline bodies of water, such as Nevada's Pyramid Lake, tufa has formed mounds, veneers and pavements, but not the mushrooming rocks, knobby spires and pillared ruins that so enchant Mono Lake's visitors. All were fashioned by freshwater springs bubbling up through Mono's carbonated brine and brine-saturated sands. Marooned on shore by receding waters, they seem like the bones of the shrinking lake.

Tufa tower on Mono Lake's northwest shore. As the tower was exposed, fresh springwater continued to flow down its flanks into the lake, forming the shelf-like flanges.

Viki Lang

Delicate sand tufa formed in the sand beneath Mono Lake.

Tufa, like stalagtites and stalagmites, is composed of calcite (calcium carbonate), the principal mineral in limestone. Its formation is basically a chemical process, although algae influence form and texture. Even at extremely low concentrations, calcium and carbonate combine into a solid and precipitate out of solution as calcite or aragonite. In Mono's brine, calcium in spring water combines with carbonates in the lakewater, forming tufa.

The tufa structure, when viewed through a microscope, reveals the shapes of algal cells. In the course of photosynthesis, algae alter Mono Lake's chemical equilibrium and facilitate tufa formation. In the process the tiny algal cells are encased in limestone caskets.[8]

In a sense, then, tufa towers are "fossilized" underwater springs. Hundreds of feet above Mono's beaches, ancient tufa mark the sites where springs welled up beneath the ice-age lake. Along some of the lakeshores, springs still gush from the tufa they formed. Israel Russell describes a spring "in the top of a tufa dome which rises about three feet above the lake surface and overflows, fountain-like, into the surrounding alkaline water;" the fountain was of "exceptional purity."* In Mono's depths, tufa continues to grow around the remaining lakebottom springs.

Tufa takes shape, not only within Mono's waters, but within the sand beneath the lake as well. Lakeshore sands and silts are saturated with brine. As fresh, calcium-bearing groundwater wells up through these sediments, it forms tufa-cemented sand tubes and columns. Along Mono's south shore, winds have stripped away the sand, exposing the delicate, waist-high *sand tufa*. Their formation beneath the lake's shores is purely a chemical process, for algae cannot grow where sunlight does not penetrate.

Despite our knowledge of their origins, Mono's tufa are still

---

*This spring has been left high and dry by the lake's receding waters.

mysterious. How old are the towers? The sand tufa? How fast do they form? Why are the towers on the north shore so different from those on the south shore? Are more concealed in the depths of the lake? Why are the ice-age tufa adorned with prism-like (thinolite) crystals? To these and many other questions, we still have no answers.

SNOWFIELDS AND SAGEBRUSH

"It has always seemed improbable," writes Gray Brechin, "a vast indigo plate in the grey desert," a lake where climatically no lake should be. A scant six to thirteen inches of precipitation fall on Mono's shores in an average year—enough to nurture sagebrush, but not trees and certainly not a permanent body of water. The lake's lifeblood springs from the west—the snowfields of the nearby Sierra Nevada.[9]

Martin Litton

Looking west across Mono Lake toward Mammoth, Negit Island in the foreground and Paoha Island in the middle distance. The white areas are alkali shoals exposed by the drawdown of the lake. In 1977 a landbridge (foreground) reached Negit Island, exposing its gull colony to mainland predators.

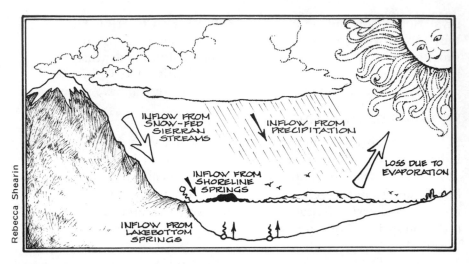

Rebecca Shearin

Figure 2. Since Mono Lake lacks an outlet and is underlain with impervious rock, water can leave only through evaporation into the atmosphere. Under natural conditions inflow from streams, springs and precipitation more or less balances evaporation. With stream diversions siphoning off 60 percent of the inflow, however, evaporation has gained the upper hand, causing the lake to drop at a rate of one to two feet per year.

Mono shares California's wet winter and dry summer *Mediterranean climate.* Eighty percent of its precipitation falls between November and April, primarily as snow. Winter storms rolling off the Pacific Ocean frequently leave two feet of snow along the lakeshores and several times as much in the Sierra. During the calm, cold days after storms, a dense sea of fog envelops the lake and laps against its cradling mountains. Called *poconip* by the Paiute, it clothes shrubs, trees and other objects with icy white crystals of extraordinary delicacy. In spring and fall, vigorous winds herald the changing seasons, reaching velocities of up to 100 miles per hour. Warm summer days conjure towering thunderheads from cloudless dawns; thunderstorms bring a little relief from the prevailingly dry conditions.

Winter storms usually blanket Mono's Sierran watershed in a deep snowpack. The higher parts of the Rush and Lee Vining Creek drainages garner up to 35 feet of snow in an average year—about 50 inches of precipitation—much more than most east slope localities. The reason is favorable geography. The Mono Basin is propitiously set to the north of Agnew Pass, a relatively low, 10,000-foot high gap in the Sierran crest that separates the North Fork of the San Joaquin River from Rush Creek. Clouds sweep up the San Joaquin Canyon, past Devil's Postpile and over the gap to leave much of their moisture on the east slope of the Sierra (to the delight of skiers at

June and Mammoth Mountains). The snowpack waters Rush, Lee
Vining and the other streams that, until humans intervened, flowed
across the sagebrush plain to feed Mono Lake.

Mono's weather is predictably unpredictable. Some winters are
wet, others dry. In 1969, for example, ten feet of snow accumulated
along the lakeshore; Sierran runoff was twice the historic average. In
1977, virtually no snow fell and runoff dropped to half of average.

FLUCTUATING LAKE LEVELS

"Half a dozen little mountain brooks flow into Mono Lake,"
exclaimed Mark Twain, "but not a stream of any kind flows out of
it. . . . What it does with its surplus water is a dark and bloody mys-
tery." The answer is simple: evaporation. Every year roughly 40
inches of water evaporate from Mono's surface—more than three feet
from each acre of lake. Because Mono covers 40,000 acres, the sun
and wind collect about 120,000 acre-feet annually.[10] Before Rush,
Lee Vining and other creeks were diverted, inflow from streams,
springs, rain and snow balanced this evaporative loss. Hence the lake
level remained more or less constant from year to year (Figure 2).

This is not to say it never varied. Each year Mono Lake used to
rise one to three feet with the snowmelt, reaching a peak between
May and early August. As temperatures rose and streamflows dwindled, evaporation gained the upper hand. From late summer through
the dog days of autumn, the lake dropped, usually reaching a low
stand in late fall.

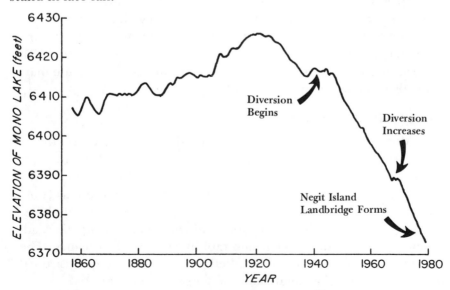

Figure 3. Surface elevations of Mono Lake, 1857–1980.[11]

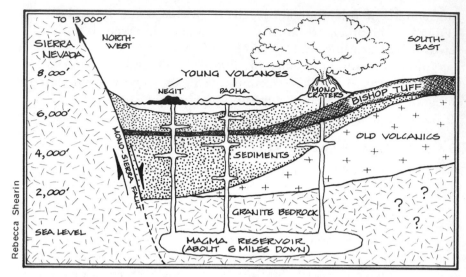

Rebecca Shearin

Figure 4. Idealized geologic cross-section of the Mono Basin. During the past three and one-half million years, the basin has slipped downwards over 11,000 vertical feet along the Mono-Sierra fault. It has filled with more than 4,000 feet of sediment washed out of the mountains. Volcanoes have repeatedly darkened its skies. Within the last ten centuries Negit, Paoha and the Mono Craters have all been in full eruption. Today these processes—faulting, erosion and volcanism— are still actively molding and changing the landscape.[13]

Over long periods of time, a series of wet, dry, warm or cold years would cause the lake to rise or fall many feet. During the ice ages, for instance, Mono swelled to several times its present size and depth. In 1857, when its shores were first surveyed, it stood at an elevation close to 6,407 feet.[11] During the following 70 years, a preponderance of wet winters raised the lake to 6,428 feet in 1927. The dry 1930s brought it down ten feet. Then came diversions and man-made drought, as we shall learn in Chapter 4 (Figure 3).

GEOLOGICAL HISTORY

Mono is one of the oldest continuously existing lakes on the North American continent. Yet compared to the age of the earth, it is young. If our planet had been born a day ago, Mono would only be about one minute (three million years) old—about as old as Homo sapiens. If that "minute" were projected on a screen, we would see a thrilling series of belching volcanoes and wrenching earthquakes, advancing and retreating glaciers and rapidly changing landscapes. The lake itself would rise and fall hundreds of feet, a "geologic heartbeat" pulsing to changes in climate and the passage of millenia.[12]

For the past ten million years, the block that forms the Sierra

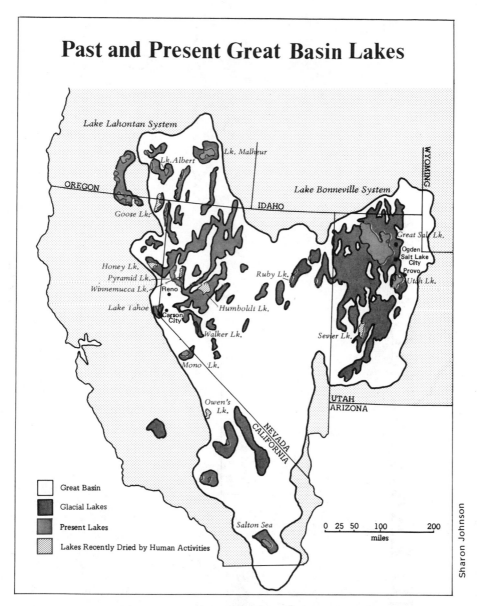

Past and Present Great Basin Lakes

Lake Lahontan System

Lk. Malheur

Lk. Albert

WYOMING

OREGON

Lake Bonneville System

IDAHO

Goose Lk.

Great Salt Lk.

Ogden
Salt Lake
City
Provo
Utah Lk.

Honey Lk.

Ruby Lk.

Pyramid Lk.

Winnemucca Lk.

Reno

Lake Tahoe

Carson
City

Humboldt Lk.

Walker Lk.

Sevier Lk.

Mono Lk.

UTAH
ARIZONA

Owen's
Lk.

NEVADA
CALIFORNIA

Great Basin

Glacial Lakes

Present Lakes

Lakes Recently Dried by Human Activities

Salton Sea

0 25 50 100   200
miles

Sharon Johnson

Map 2. Mono Lake lies at the western edge of the Great Basin. Throughout this arid region, streams do not drain to the ocean, but vanish in desert valleys or collect in saline lakes without outlets, of which Mono, Pyramid and Great Salt Lakes are the best known. Many of the basin lakes have been dried up by human activities; all the rest, like Mono Lake, are threatened. During the ice-ages, vast inland seas filled the troughs between mountain ranges and covered much of present-day Utah and western Nevada.

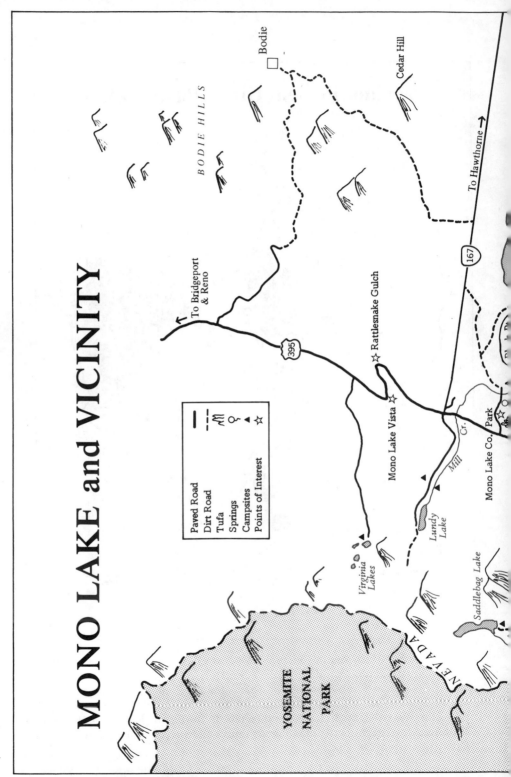

Map 3. The Mono Lake watershed.

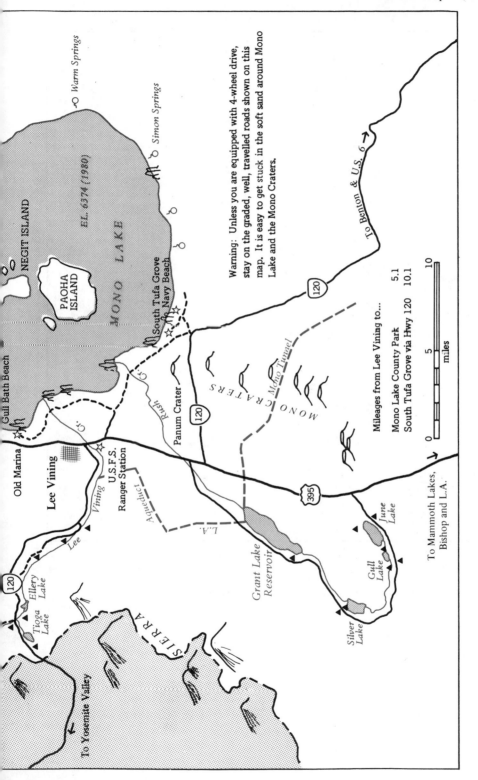

Warning: Unless you are equipped with 4-wheel drive, stay on the graded, well, travelled roads shown on this map. It is easy to get stuck in the soft sand around Mono Lake and the Mono Craters.

Mileages from Lee Vining to...

Mono Lake County Park	5.1
South Tufa Grove via Hwy 120	10.1

Sharon Johnson

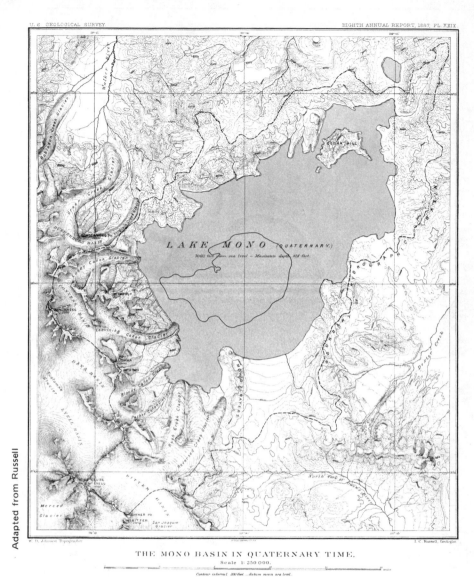

Adapted from Russell

U. S. GEOLOGICAL SURVEY   EIGHTH ANNUAL REPORT, 1887. PL. XXIX

LAKE MONO (QUATERNARY.)
7060 feet above sea level – Maximum depth 824 feet.

THE MONO BASIN IN QUATERNARY TIME.
Scale 1: 250 000.
Contour interval 200 feet ...datum mean sea level.

Map 4. At maximum size, ice-age Mono Lake covered 338 square miles and reached a depth of almost 1,000 feet—five times larger and six times deeper than the modern lake.[16]

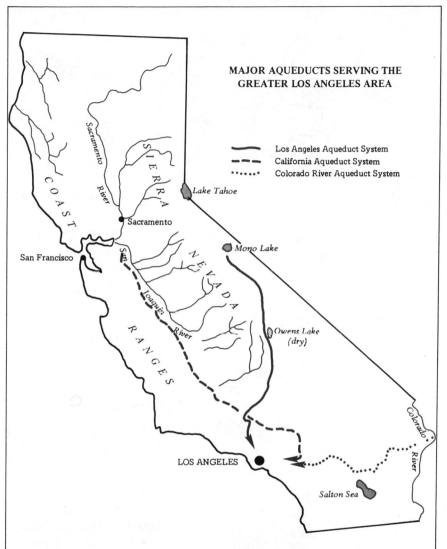

MAJOR AQUEDUCTS SERVING THE
GREATER LOS ANGELES AREA

Los Angeles Aqueduct System
California Aqueduct System
Colorado River Aqueduct System

Lake Tahoe

Sacramento

San Francisco

Mono Lake

Owens Lake
(dry)

Colorado River

LOS ANGELES

Salton Sea

Sharon Johnson

Map 5. Water diverted from the Mono Basin travels down the east side of the
Sierra Nevada, past the dry bed of Owens Lake and on to Los Angeles. The city
obtains water from northern California and the Colorado River as well.

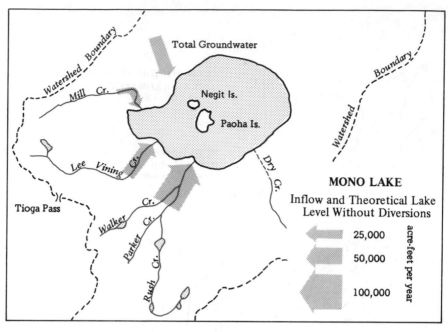

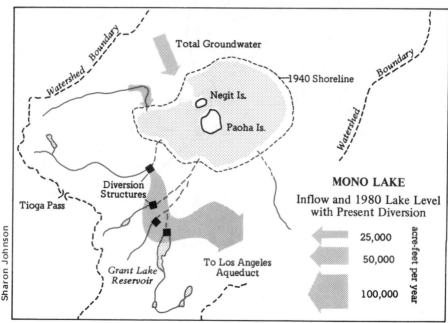

Map 6. Water is diverted into the Los Angeles Aqueduct from all but one of the major streams which feed Mono Lake. The upper map depicts the watershed without diversions. The lower map depicts the diversion points, quantity of water currently being exported and the impact on Mono Lake's size.[7] Since diversions began, the lake has fallen 45 feet, its volume has been halved, salinity has doubled and Negit Island has become connected to the mainland.

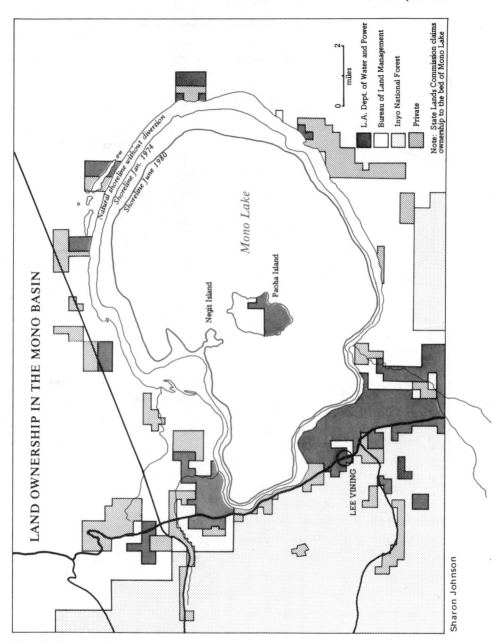

LAND OWNERSHIP IN THE MONO BASIN

L.A. Dept. of Water and Power
Bureau of Land Management
Inyo National Forest
Private

Note: State Lands Commission claims ownership to the bed of Mono Lake

miles

Mono Lake

Natural shoreline without diversion
Shoreline Jan. 1974
Shoreline June 1980

Negit Island

Paoha Island

LEE VINING

Sharon Johnson

Map 7. Most of the land in the Mono Basin is publicly owned. In the 1930s Los Angeles purchased farms and ranches in order to secure water rights to the basin's streams.

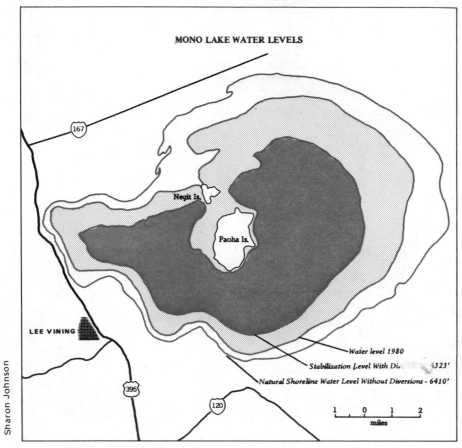

Sharon Johnson

Map 8. At present diversion rates, Mono Lake is projected to drop another 50 feet before it stabilizes at one-third its natural surface area and less than one-fifth its natural volume. Long before it stabilizes, if it ever does, the lake will become a birdless chemical sump and alkali dustbowl.

PLATE TECTONICS AND THE MONO BASIN

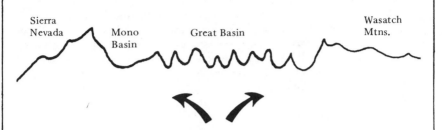

Sierra Nevada — Mono Basin — Great Basin — Wasatch Mtns.

    Geologists now believe that the crust of the earth, rather than being immobile, is composed of plates that move about the planet colliding with one another (plate tectonics). The westward movement of the North American plate over the Pacific plate spawned the forces that uplifted the Great Basin, pulled it asunder and created the Mono Basin. The relationship between plate tectonics and the modern landscape, however, is exceedingly complicated and hotly debated. One theory, simply stated, postulates that the western part of the North American plate has drifted over an oceanic spreading center. As a result, the Sierra Nevada and Wasatch Mountains are moving away from each other and the crust in between is collapsing and fragmenting, forming the basins and ranges of the Great Basin.[24]

Nevada has been rising and tilting to the west. Until about four million years ago, however, the precipitous eastern Sierran escarpment did not exist; you could have strolled from the crest east into Nevada. There was no Mono Basin and no Mono Lake. The modern landscape was molded, not by the uplift of the Sierra, but primarily by the dropping of the basin. For several million years, the basin has been tilting westwards due to downward slippage along a fault at the foot of the Sierra. It has dropped about 11,000 feet, two vertical miles, at a rate of three to four feet per thousand years (Figure 4, p. 26).[13]

    Why, then, doesn't the Sierra tower 11,000 rather than 6,000 feet above the floor of the Mono Basin? The answer is erosion and deposition. The Mono Basin is half-filled with silt, sand and gravel. For example, in 1972 a well drilled on the lake's south shore struck granite bedrock at a depth of 4,000 feet.[14]

    As the Mono Basin's western floor slipped downwards along the Mono-Sierran fault, its southern and northern margins tilted slowly towards its center. This downwarping, gentle compared to that along the Sierra, cradled the basin with rolling uplands to the north, east and south. The "bathtub" filled with water to form Mono Lake.

    Even before the Mono Basin came into existence, the climate

HOW OLD IS MONO LAKE?

A well sunk on Paoha Island in 1908 affords a clue to Mono Lake's age. It was drilled for oil, but only uncovered sediments and, at a depth of about 1,400 feet, a "light pink rock, very hard." This pink rock was Bishop tuff, a volcanic ash erupted 730,000 years ago (see section on "Volcanoes and Volcanic Islands"). Above and below the pink-hued tuff were layers of sediment washed into the lake from the surrounding uplands. If Mono had dried up in the last 700,000 years, there would have been layers of salts in this sedimentary record. The lack of such a saline layer indicates the lake's persistence over millenia—at least 730,000 years and probably much longer.[23]

Few lakes on earth are hundreds of thousands of years old. The Great Lakes, for instance, date from the end of the last ice-age only 13,000 years ago. Oregon's Crater Lake was formed by volcanic eruptions about 7,000 years ago. Great Salt Lake, while as old as Mono, has dried up many times. Mono, in contrast, has never fallen much below its present low ebb. Only Lake Tahoe has remained a more permanent part of North America's waterscape.

Other parts of the world do harbor older bodies of water. Asia's Lake Baikal, for instance, is at least 50 million years of age.

Kenneth Lajoie

These layered sediments, exposed along Wilson Creek west of Black Point, were deposited beneath the waters of ice-age Mono Lake 12,500 (top) to 23,000 (bottom) years ago. Near the top is a thick, dark layer of ash from the Black Point eruption of 13,800 years ago. Below are light-colored Sierran sediments interspersed with narrow bands of dark-colored ash from eruptions of the Mono Craters.[28]

was becoming colder and drier. Ten million years ago redwood forests clothed much of the region. But the Sierra rose up to block Pacific storms, leaving the land to the east in a rain shadow. Redwoods and ferns gave way to drought-resistant oaks and chaparral, and finally to pinyon pines and sagebrush.[15]

In its infancy, Mono Lake may have drained to the south or east. Sometime in its youth, as its basin deepened and aridity increased, it ceased overflowing and became a sea without an outlet. Excepting brief interludes, it has been landlocked ever since.

DURING THE ICE AGES

The slopes above Mono Lake are etched with well-defined, horizontal beach terraces cut by the waves of a much larger lake during the ice ages. About 13,000 years ago, fed by melting Sierran glaciers, the Mono Basin bathtub filled to its brim and even overflowed for a brief time. It became a vast inland sea 28 miles long by 18 miles broad that reached eastwards into Nevada. Cedar Hill, a million-year-old volcano straddling the stateline north of Highway 167, became an island. The lake covered 338 square miles—over 40 percent of its drainage basin—and reached a depth of over 900 feet (Map 4, p. 30). Its waters were nearly fresh, although devoid of fish.*[16]

Throughout the Great Basin, vast inland seas filled the troughs between mountain ranges. Basins that are now parched and dry cradled bodies of water as large or larger than present-day Mono. Lake Bonneville, for instance, covered 20,000 square miles of Utah, eastern Nevada and southern Idaho, Lake Lahontan 8,000 square miles of northwest Nevada (Map 2, p. 27). When Mono overflowed, it drained into lakes in Adobe, Owens, Searles, Panamint and ultimately Death Valleys.

Mono Lake probably filled its basin only during the interludes when glaciers were melting back up mountain canyons—interludes measured in centuries. During the height of the Sierran glaciations, which lasted for millenia, the lake stood roughly 400 feet above its present level and 300 feet below its spill elevation—about as high as the town of Lee Vining (6,800'). As the glaciers retreated, the flood of meltwater swelled the lake to maximum size. Then, as stream flows dwindled, it shrank rapidly, dropping at a rate of many feet per year.[17]

Imagine the splendor of that ice-age lake! "The peaks of the Sierra," wrote Israel Russell, "were white with snow throughout the

---

*Many writers use the name "Lake Russell" to designate the ice-age lake. I prefer "ice-age Mono Lake," for it emphasizes the uninterrupted existence of this body of water through hundreds of thousands of climatic fluctuations.

year and gave birth to ice rivers of great magnitude, some of which reached [Mono's] shores." Icebergs calved from glaciers may have drifted into present-day Nevada.

From his study of the eastern Sierra's glacial moraines, Russell concluded that there had been more than one advance of the glaciers and expansion of Mono Lake. Geologists now recognize at least four

MONO LAKE SINCE THE ICE-AGE

Viki Lang

Tufa-coated tree stumps exposed in 1960 by Mono's receding waters. These trees were drowned by a rise in the lake about 920 years ago.

Since the last ice age ended about 12,000 years ago, Mono Lake has remained relatively low, but has continued to fluctuate in response to changes in climate. Five thousand years ago, the lake fell to a low stand of about 6,365 feet, then rose to 6,497 feet about 2,500 years later.[25]

While the Mono Lake of 5,000 years ago probably stood at a lower elevation than the modern lake, it may have held a greater volume of water and hence have been less saline. At that time neither Negit nor Paoha Islands had erupted into existence. When the islands were born, they must have displaced a substantial volume of water and raised the lake 20 to 30 feet.[26]

In 1960, Mono Lake's receding waters exposed a clue to its recent fluctuations: a grove of tufa-coated tree stumps rooted at an elevation of about 6,400 feet. Carbon dating revealed that the grove had been killed about 920 years ago, presumably by a rise in the lake. Unless the stumps had been submerged during the succeeding millenium, they would have quickly decomposed (as they have since 1960). Around the year 1,000, when the stumps were flourishing trees, Mono must have stood below 6,400 feet. This was the time of the "medieval maxima," a period of warm, dry conditions over much of the earth when, for example, Scandinavian farmers settled in Greenland. During the ensuing centuries, the climate flip-flopped into a "little ice-age" that froze out the Greenlanders, spawned mini-glaciers in the Sierra and swelled Mono Lake to 6,455 feet by about 1700—82 feet above its 1981 level.[26]

major Sierran "ice-ages" during the past million years. Some day the ice may return.

VOLCANOES AND VOLCANIC ISLANDS

"Mono Craters May Be Next Mt. St. Helens" headlined a recent article in the *San Francisco Chronicle*. The prediction is well-founded. Volcanoes have been erupting in and around Mono Lake for millions of years. Only a century ago puffs of sulfurous fumes rose from its surface.[18] Hot springs still steam along its shores. At Paoha Island's Hot Springs Cove, noxious vapors hiss out of holes and crevices. Some day, perhaps in our lifetimes, the earth will reawaken and fill Mono's skies with fire and ash.

Volcanoes were erupting in the Mono region long before the lake was born. Cowtrack Mountain, the Anchorite Hills and the Bodie Hills are the weathered remains of volcanic flows dating back three to twelve million years.

One of the most violent eruptions of which we have record swept over Mono about 730,000 years ago. Millions of tons of incandescent ash and hot gas exploded from the immense Long Valley caldera, a large crater directly south of Mono Basin. The ash encircled the globe, accumulating in layers as far east as Nebraska. Between Bishop and Mono Lake this catastrophic eruption left a mantle of pinkish rock hundreds of feet deep—the Bishop tuff. This rock is exposed in pot-holed, wind-polished outcrops, the Aeolian Buttes, between Highway

*Along Highway 395 north of the June Lake Junction, a small sign points out the Aeolian Buttes, but erroneously calls them "the oldest volcanic formations in the Mono Basin."

Frasher's Photography

Paoha's crater lakelets. Heart and McPherson "Lakes" occupied volcanic craters on the northeast side of the island. They were fed by Mono Lake water seeping through the island's porous sediments. In the 1960s, as the lake receded, the lakelets dried into salt pans.

395 and the Mono Craters, and along the southeastern rim of the basin.* Elsewhere the tuff has been covered by younger volcanics, glacial moraines and outwash from the mountains.[19]

From any distance the weathered Aeolian Buttes, Bodie Hills and Cowtrack Mountains look more like hills than volcanoes. Not so the symmetrical cones and jagged flows of the Mono Craters. "So perfect are their shapes and so fresh is their appearance," wrote Israel Russell, "the eye lingers about their summits in half expectation of seeing wreaths of vapor or the lurid light of molten lava ascending from their throats." Most of these craters, Russell concluded, must have erupted since the ebb of the ice-age lake, for there are no wave-cut terraces incised in their flanks. While their history does date back 40,000 years, most are relatively young. Panum Crater was blasted only 640 years ago, the high turret-shaped cones around the time of Christ.[20]

Volcanoes have even erupted within Mono's waters. The most remarkable, Black Point, rises like a dark-colored groundswell from the north shore. Thirteen thousand years ago it sputtered beneath the ice-age lake, never quite breaking the surface. Its summit cracked into fissures two to three feet wide and 30 to 50 feet in depth that are bizarrely veneered in bubbly white tufa. Soon after its fiery birth, the ebbing waters of the lake left Black Point an island and then a peninsula. Nowhere else on earth is an underwater volcano so fully exposed.[21]

Within the last thousand years volcanoes exploded again in Mono's depths to form its two dramatically contrasting islands.[22] The larger white island, Paoha, looks more like a badlands than a volcano. Water and wind have gullied its 2,000 acres into a labyrinth of raw-looking bluffs, ridges and ravines. Except at Hot Springs Cove, where foul-tasting springs water a boggy meadow, the island is scantily clothed in spiny greasewood and tufts of cheat grass. On windy days clouds of dust blow off its bony hills. Even when the air is calm, mysterious whirlwinds scour its shoals. It is a lonely place, yet hauntingly beautiful.

Most of Paoha Island is covered, not with lava or ash, but with whitish lakebottom sediments. These sediments are composed of clays, silts and the remains of one-celled, microscopic plants called diatoms that lived (and still live) in Mono's waters. Some of the diatom beds are 20 to 30 feet thick. Only at the north end of the island and at Hot Springs Cove are Paoha's volcanic origins evidenced by dark-colored cinder cones and lava flows. As lava rose and spread beneath the lake, the light-colored lakebottom sediments were thrust above the surface.

Paoha's black sister island, Negit, was formed about the same time. Its symmetrical cone and jagged lava flows are unmistakably volcanic. To the northeast, small volcanic islets break Mono's surface.

The birth of Mono's islands was accompanied by incandescent lava flows, violent explosions and boiling clouds of steam and ash. There were several eruptive phases, beginning with obsidian (volcanic glass) flows on the north end of Paoha and concluding with a surge of lava down Negit's cone.

Sometime in the past, eruptions may have annihilated fish and other lifeforms from an ancestral Mono Lake.* Brine shrimp, brine flies and algae must weather such calamities, at least in numbers sufficient to replenish the lake.

Diatom from Paoha Island, magnified 500 times.

United States Geological Survey

---

*No fish of any kind are native to the Mono Basin; trout were introduced to its fresh waters by miners and settlers in the nineteenth century.

3

The Living Sea

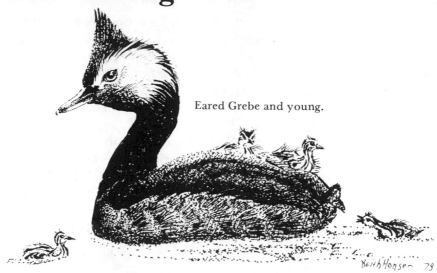

Eared Grebe and young.

On a July afternoon, two biologists canoe along Mono's shores. In the distance a flock of small shorebirds appears above the placid blue water. "For the next hour," writes Chris Swarth, "we watched thousands of Wilson's Phalaropes drop out of the sky. Flocks coalesced with flocks into mile-long streams of thousands of birds. We tallied close to 24,000 crossing the lake to south shore feeding areas, their white underparts flashing in the setting sun."

For untold millenia phalaropes and other water birds have flocked to Mono to rest, feed, raise young and molt worn feathers. Dubbed by Mark Twain the "dead sea of California," the lake is actually teeming with life. With the help of sunlight, algae grow and mlltiply in its waters. The algae are grazed by vast herds of brine shrimp and brine flies. These, in turn, nourish innumerable birds (Figure 5).

FEW SPECIES, COUNTLESS INDIVIDUALS

In spite of Mono's fecundity, surprisingly few species dwell in the lake. The fisherman who casts his worm-baited line into the briny water soon reels in—a dead worm. In the 1940s California Fish and Game tried planting trout. The hapless fish "made three jumps and then turned belly up."[1] Neither fish nor worm can survive, but shrimp, flies and microscopic life thrive in phenomenal abundance.

Figure 5. Mono Lake's food web. Microscropic algae capture the sun's energy through a process called photosynthesis. Brine shrimp and brine flies feed on the algae, and are eaten in turn by millions of birds. When the algae, flies and birds die, they are decomposed by bottom-dwelling bacteria. This *detritus* fertilizes the algae, and so the circle goes round.

You need not be a biologist to sense this fecundity. Just try to tally Mono's brine shrimp and brine flies. At peak densities over 50,000 brine shrimp crowd a cubic yard of lakewater; the overall population exceeds four trillion individuals and weighs over six million pounds dry weight.[2] Brine flies darken the shore for mile after mile; four thousand have been tallied in a square foot.[3] "Their buzz," wrote J. Ross Browne in 1865, "sounds like the brewing of a distant storm."

In comparison freshwater lakes are biological deserts. For example, compare Mono with Lake Tahoe. Tahoe drains via the Truckee River into the Lahontan Basin; Mono has no outlet. Tahoe's waters are fresh; those of Mono are saline and alkaline. Tahoe supports nine species of native fish, dozens of invertebrates and vascular plants, and more than a hundred microscopic species; Mono supports no fish or vascular plants, only three invertebrates visible to the naked eye, and fewer than 30 species of microscopic life. Yet in terms of numbers, Mono is a crowded metropolis, Tahoe a small town. Why does a salty sea nourish few species in great abundance?

To begin with, Mono's unusual chemistry limits the number of species that can live in its waters. The cells of all living things, from algae to gulls to humans, are bathed in fluids that are chemically similar to seawater. In Mono's water, carbonates and other substances are many times more concentrated. Only a handful of species have evolved a means of keeping these substances below toxic levels within their cells. They "pump" the substances out of their bodies, a process called *osmoregulation.*

Mono Lake's inhabitants are efficient osmoregulators. Despite the energy costs of running the "pumps," they grow and multiply at astonishing rates. Something in the lake's chemistry must counterbalance the osmotic handicaps imposed by salinity.

It may be the phosphates and other nutrients that, like salts, have been collecting in Mono's water for millenia, cycling and recycling through the lake's living community. Bottom-dwelling bacteria play a key role by decomposing dead algae, brine shrimp and other organic matter (detritus) that drifts down into the lake's dark depths. By breaking down complex organic molecules, bacteria make phosphates and other nutrients available to the algae, promoting their growth.[4]

Because so few species inhabit Mono's waters, they propagate large populations. Few species mean few competitors for food and other resources. Most of Mono's algae are cropped by only two animals, brine fly larvae and brine shrimp. Hence the numbers of flies and shrimp are astronomical.

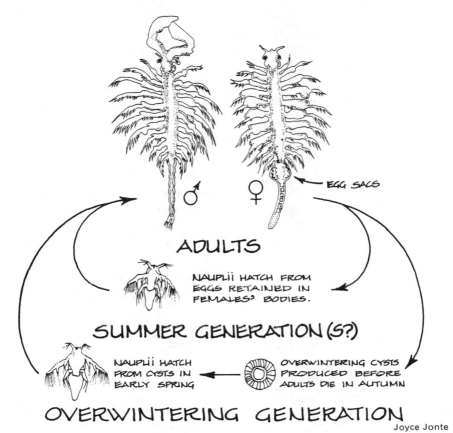

EGG SACS

ADULTS

NAUPLII HATCH FROM
EGGS RETAINED IN
FEMALES' BODIES.

SUMMER GENERATION (S?)

NAUPLII HATCH
FROM CYSTS IN
EARLY SPRING

OVERWINTERING CYSTS
PRODUCED BEFORE
ADULTS DIE IN AUTUMN

OVERWINTERING GENERATION

Joyce Jonte

Figure 6. Life cycle of Mono Lake's brine shrimp. Eggs hatch into miniatures, called *nauplii,* which reach shrimphood in 8–12 weeks. Most adults die in autumn, but not before producing eggs, called *cysts,* which hatch into nauplii the following spring.

BRINE SHRIMP VS. ALGAE

Mark Twain characterized Mono's brine shrimp as "white feathery worms, one half-inch long, which look like bits of thread frayed out at the sides." Their bodies are colorful, ranging in hue from ochre to turquoise. Elongate, tapering trunks are fringed with eleven pairs of feathery appendages which continually scull the water. This graceful, symmetrical motion propels the shrimp while they gather food. As they swim, water is forced towards their trunks, where algae are filtered out and swept forward into their mouths.

The brine shrimp spawn at least two generations a year: a first hatched from overwintering eggs, called cysts, in March, and a second in late May and June (there may be a third in late summer). The females either retain the fertilized eggs within their bodies until they hatch or release them as cysts. From July through September, trillions of cysts rain into Mono's bottom muck (Figure 6).

During early fall, as Mono's waters chill, most of the adult shrimp die or are eaten by grebes. While icy winds whip across the lake, algae grow and multiply. With no shrimp grazing them, the algal "bloom" turns the lake pea-soup green. Then, in March, the cysts hatch into miniature shrimp, called *nauplii* (singular: *nauplius*), and swarm to the surface. Development is slow in the gradually warming, but still frigid water. Eight to twelve weeks and fourteen molts later, the nauplii reach shrimphood and begin spawning a second generation.[5]

By June, herds of brine shrimp have grazed away the algae. As the algal pastures dwindle, the lakewater clears. Visibility, two to three feet in winter, increases tenfold. Swimmers delight in the lake's clarity.

Fortunately for the algae, the summer sun does not heat Mono's depths. Below about 30 feet, temperatures remain around 40°F.

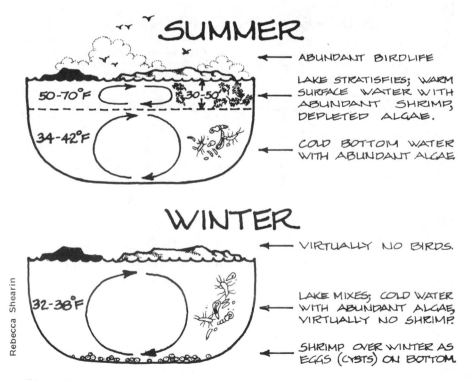

Figure 7. In summer Mono Lake stratifies into two layers that don't mix: an upper, well-oxygenated layer of warm temperatures, abundant shrimp and depleted algae, and a deep region of cold temperatures, little oxygen, very few shrimp and numerous algae. In winter the surface water chills and sinks, causing the lake to mix from top to bottom. Shrimp vanish and algae thrive.

MONO BRINE SHRIMP: A UNIQUE SPECIES?

Mono's brine shrimp have adapted genetically to a lake unlike any other on earth. They are so attuned osmotically to Mono's chemistry, for instance, that they perish in most other brine shrimp habitats. Conversely brine shrimp from Great Salt Lake, San Francisco Bay and other localities cannot survive in Mono's waters. Unlike other brine shrimp, the Mono variety produce eggs that sink to the bottom and hatch at low temperatures. Most populations produce floating eggs that hatch in relatively warm water. For these and other reasons, most biologists consider Mono's shrimp a separate species, *Artemia monica.*[19]

Since warm water is lighter than cold, the lake becomes thermally stratified into two layers that don't mix: an upper, well-oxygenated layer of warm temperatures, abundant shrimp and depleted algae, and a deep region of cold temperatures, little oxygen, very few shrimp, but numerous algae. Since there is scarcely any light at these depths, the algae spend the summer in a state like suspended animation. Frosty autumn weather ends their exile by chilling Mono's surface and depleting the shrimp. The now colder surface water sinks and the lake mixes from top to bottom, bringing nutrients and algae to the surface and fertilizing the algal bloom (Figure 7).[6]

BRINE FLIES, MIDGES AND MONSTERS

Sharing Mono's shallows with the shrimp are bottom-dwelling, immature brine flies, the offspring of the small flies that swarm along the shores. Harmless and fascinating, brine flies want nothing from humans, disdaining even to land on sun-bathers. They just go about their business, lapping up algae from the muddy shores, walking out to sea on the surface film, and entering the lake to lay their eggs on submerged tufa. They are fodder for thousands of shorebirds and were once a staple for humans as well.

Female brine flies envelop themselves in a globule of air and crawl underwater by clinging to tufa or some other solid object. After laying a few dozen eggs, they simply let go and, as Mark Twain faithfully records, "pop up to the surface as dry as a patent-office report, and walk off as unconcernedly as if they had been educated especially with a view to offering instructive entertainment to man in that particular way."

The eggs hatch into wriggly, worm-like *larvae* that crawl about submerged rocks and tufa with the aid of clawed legs. They feed by scraping off algae. After three molts and several weeks of growth, the larvae clamp themselves onto rocks. Their outer skin hardens into

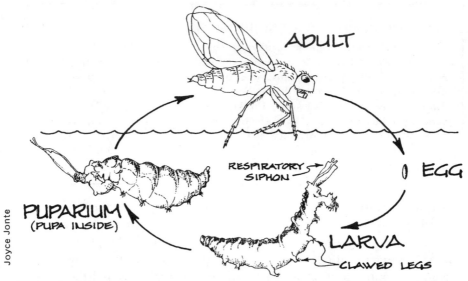

ADULT

RESPIRATORY SIPHON

PUPARIUM
(PUPA INSIDE)

EGG

LARVA

CLAWED LEGS

Joyce Jonte

Figure 8. Life cycle of the brine fly. Females crawl underwater to lay eggs, which hatch into wriggly aquatic larvae. After fattening on algae for several weeks, the larvae secure themselves to tufa, pupate and emerge weeks later as winged adults.

brown, spindle-shaped *pupariums* analogous to butterfly cocoons. In one to three weeks the *pupae,* as the larvae are called at this stage, turn from worm-like creatures into winged adults. The space left within their pupariums fills with air. As a consequence, the emerging flies float to the surface to begin new lives enveloped in air bubbles (Figure 8).

Two to three generations of brine flies hatch on Mono's shores each year. After autumn cold dooms the adults, dormant larvae and pupae sustain the population through the winter.[7]

A few other organisms may await discovery in Mono's depths. In 1976 the larvae of a small midge were encountered swimming with rapid eel-like movements about the edges of tufa.[8] In 1946 a State Fish and Game biologist found "worms" in the bottom mud off Paoha (the "bloodworms" oldtimers talk about?).[9] Sightings of a "Mono Monster" (a twenty-ton brine shrimp?) date back to Paiute times. But algae, shrimp, flies and birds are clearly the dominant actors in Mono's evolutionary theater.

NESTING GULLS AND PLOVERS

Seventy-nine species of water bird, just about every North American shorebird, duck, grebe and gull, visit Mono's shores.[10] For five species in particular the lake is of critical importance: nesting California Gulls and Snowy Plovers, and migrating Wilson's Phalaropes,

LIFE IN THE GULL COLONY

William Leon Dawson visited Negit Island in 1919. The following description of life in the gull colony was published in his four-volume classic, *The Birds of California,* in 1924:

There was life at an intense node—a thousand irate fathers beating the air with futile wing, and venting their rage in incomprehensible cackles and kawks, while a thousand anxious mothers hovered or settled by turns, their hearts wrung by the importunities of a thousand chicks in very moment of entering this bubbling world. . . . A thousand births in a day in a single community, and another thousand expected on the morrow. Little time and scant welcome for visitors. . . .

But what an armed truce was there also! Call it a "community"? To be sure the birds crowd together as close as they dare, and they act together in facing a common foe. But why do they crowd together? For every beak is turned against every other beak, and the space between nests is guaranteed in every instance to be greater than the distance which can be bridged by two craning necks tipped by two pairs of hostile mandibles. Crabbed tempers have these California Gulls, and the brandished beak is the sign of welcome and the notice of departure to any other of their own kind save their wedded partners, and not infrequently to them also.

In conspicuous exception to this churlish behavior, I recall two birds whom we dubbed "the lovers," which during the whole period of our review stood side by side with their bodies in actual contact, the very picture of amiability. Perhaps gull nature varies as much as human nature, and there are happy exceptions to the universal grouch.

Eggs of the California Gull about to hatch.

Michael Dressler

Northern Phalaropes and Eared Grebes.

The birds come for easy meals. In most lakes fish predation keeps numbers of invertebrates to relatively low levels. Not so in Mono, where high productivity and the absence of fish assure bumper crops of brine shrimp and flies.

California Gulls are lured by plentiful food and (until recently) safe island nesting sanctuaries. About 50,000, 95 percent of the state's breeding population, nest at Mono Lake (Map 9).[11] With hungry mouths to feed, abundant food is a necessity. The islands protect eggs and young from coyotes, racoons, weasels and other mainland predators. Without such protection, the colonies would be annihilated—as the 1979 Negit Island tragedy sadly proves (p. 89).

A typical summer birdscape along Mono's shores. Pictured from left to right are Brewer's Blackbirds, California Gulls (flying and on tufa), Northern Phalaropes (swimming), Common Snipe (in grass), American Avocets (foreground), Wilson's Phalaropes (on shore, middle ground), Snowy Plovers (running, foreground), Killdeer (behind plovers), Eared Grebes (swimming), Northern Phalarope (swimming), Spotted Sandpiper (base of tufa) and Violet-green Swallows (flying and perched on tufa tower).

The gulls arrive in April, soaring across the Sierra Nevada when the passes are still buried in snow. Eggs are laid in May, chicks hatch in June, and by August the young and their parents are winging westwards to coastal wintering areas from British Columbia to San Diego. Many of the gulls seen about bays, schoolyards and fields were raised at Mono.[12]

The newly hatched gull chicks are helpless, hungry fluff balls. They beg for meals by pecking at the red spot on their parents' bills. In response the adults obligingly regurgitate gullet-fulls of shrimp and flies.

Who does not delight in watching flocks of gulls soaring in a blue sky? Mono's gulls are not only beautiful, they also fill an essential role in nature's economy. They scavenge Sierran lakes and streams, consuming garbage left by careless hikers and fishermen. They follow farmers' tractors, feeding on agricultural pests. Remember the Mormon farmers near Great Salt Lake whose crops were threatened by locusts? California Gulls ate the insects and saved the harvest.[13]

Liane Enkelis

California Gull regurgitating a meal to its hungry chick.

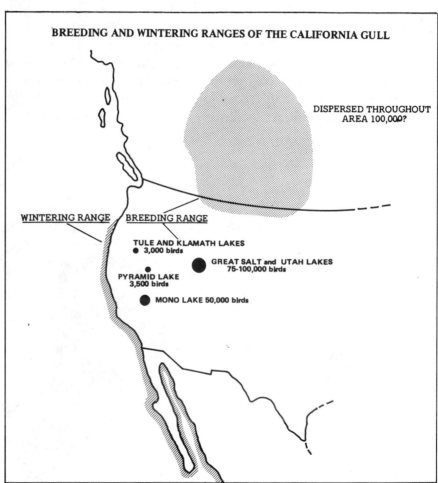

Sharon Johnson

BREEDING AND WINTERING RANGES OF THE CALIFORNIA GULL

DISPERSED THROUGHOUT AREA 100,000?

WINTERING RANGE   BREEDING RANGE

TULE AND KLAMATH LAKES
● 3,000 birds

GREAT SALT and UTAH LAKES
75-100,000 birds

PYRAMID LAKE
3,500 birds

MONO LAKE 50,000 birds

Map 9. The California Gull, one of the commonest Pacific Coast seagulls, deserts coastal beaches and valleys each spring to nest on islands in inland lakes and rivers. About one-fifth of the world population raise their young at Mono Lake. Because of the falling lake level, however, nesting islands are becoming peninsulas, exposing the colonies to mainland predators.[11]

In fact gulls will eat almost anything they can find or catch, including the eggs and young of Snowy Plovers and other ground-nesting shorebirds. To elude gulls and other predators, shorebirds rely on camouflage and trickery. Their eggs and chicks are protectively colored. When predators (or humans) approach, the adults distract their attention with noisy displays. Killdeer and Snowy Plovers even mimic crippled birds, dragging "broken" wings and whistling piteously.

About 400 Snowy Plovers, 10 percent of the entire California breeding population, nest along Mono's windswept, alkali-encrusted shores. These diminutive, delicately plumaged shorebirds are almost invisible until they flit from underfoot. Formerly numerous along Pacific beaches, the coastal population has been harried to the brink of extinction by humans, dogs and habitat destruction.

Soon after arriving in April, Snowy Plovers begin courtship and nesting. The clutch of three eggs, laid in a shallow depression scraped in the sand, weighs one-half as much as the female bird. Within hours after hatching the chicks, mere fluffs of mottled down, are able to run about—a necessity if they are to elude the perils of ploverdom. Guided by their parents the chicks scrounge their own meals, walking over two miles to choice feeding areas.[14]

TRAVELERS FROM DISTANT SHORES

Before the plovers, gulls and other nesting birds have fledged the last of their young, the first migrants arrive from the north. By the end of July, Mono's shores are alive with shorebirds. By far the most numerous, graceful and trusting are the phalaropes (făl'a-rōp).

Sit quietly, and the phalaropes will feed at your feet. Float in the lake, and the curious birds will paddle within arm's reach. Their euphonious name is Greek for "coot-foot," for, like coots and unlike other shorebirds, they have evolved lobed toes.* These propel them

Ian Tait

Nest of Snowy Plover concealed among tufa-coated rocks.

about on the water, where they daintily pick brine flies off the surface film and dab brine shrimp from the lake's upper inch. Sometimes they seem to unwind, swimming in tight little circles to stir up food. Hunched along the shore they seize passing flies with lightning thrusts of their bills, rarely missing their targets.

Phalaropes have a fascinating family life. The females wear the colorful breeding plumage and actively court the males. Then they leave the males behind to incubate eggs and raise chicks without assistance. As a consequence, female phalaropes reach Mono's shores weeks ahead of the males. Last of all come the young, on their own on their first migration.

Female Wilson's Phalaropes, still in resplendent breeding dress,

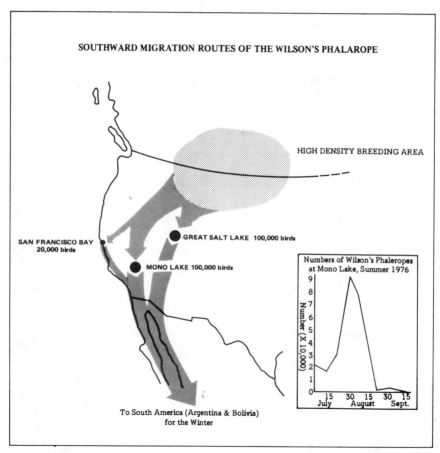

Map 10. About one-third of the world's Wilson's Phalaropes rest, feed and molt at Mono Lake during their southward migration from the Northern Plains to Bolivia and Argentina. These colorful relatives of sandpipers, like countless other water birds, depend on Mono, Great Salt and a few other highly productive saline lakes for the food they need to cross hundreds of miles of desert.[15]

arrive in July from breeding haunts in southern Canada and the intermountain west. By the time the males appear, the first female Northern Phalaropes descend from arctic tundras. In late July and early
August, the Wilson's embark for Bolivia and Argentina, leaving Northern Phalaropes in possession of the lake. A few weeks later the north-
erners are winging south as well, but not towards land. They winter
on the southern oceans, feeding on tiny crustaceans and sea animals
and occasionally picking parasites from the backs of resting whales.

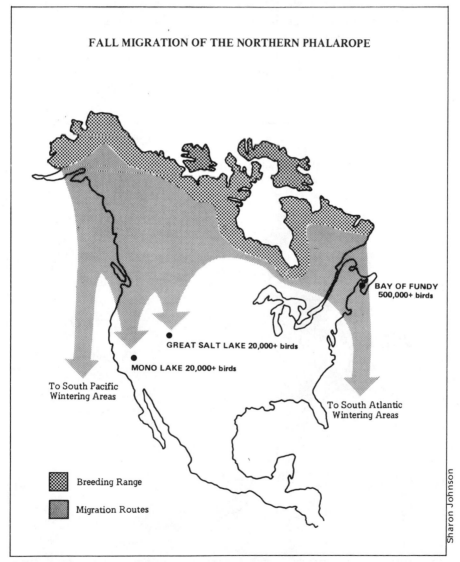

FALL MIGRATION OF THE NORTHERN PHALAROPE

BAY OF FUNDY
500,000+ birds

GREAT SALT LAKE 20,000+ birds

MONO LAKE 20,000+ birds

To South Pacific
Wintering Areas

To South Atlantic
Wintering Areas

Breeding Range

Migration Routes

Sharon Johnson

Map 11. Over 20,000 Northern Phalaropes gather on Mono Lake during their
southward migration to wintering areas on the southern oceans.[15]

For these two-ounce puffs of feathers Mono is a rest stop on journeys of thousands of miles (Maps 10 and 11).[15]

While as many as 90,000 phalaropes have been tallied on the lake, their numbers are dwarfed by flotillas of Eared Grebes. In mid-summer these duck-like diving birds arrive from breeding haunts across western Canada and the United States. By September about 700,000 are bobbing on Mono's surface (Map 12).[16]

Few birds are more beautifully adapted to aquatic life. Eared Grebes not only feed, sleep, court and mate in water, they carry their young pick-a-back under the surface. Their floating nests, built out of buoyant vegetation, adjust to rises and falls in water level. As Mono lacks aquatic vegetation, they do not nest at the lake. But it is a critical stopover on their migratory journeys to Southern California and Mexican wintering areas.

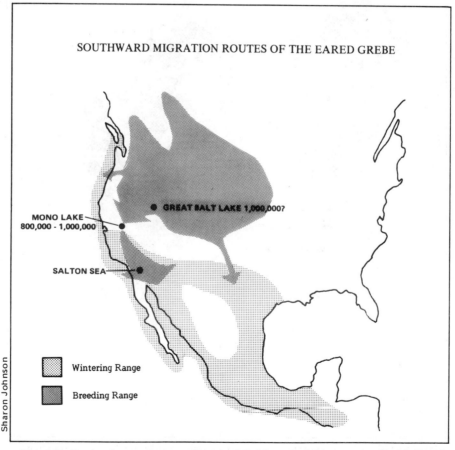

SOUTHWARD MIGRATION ROUTES OF THE EARED GREBE

GREAT SALT LAKE 1,000,000?

MONO LAKE
800,000 - 1,000,000

SALTON SEA

Wintering Range

Breeding Range

Sharon Johnson

Map 12. During late summer and early fall, Mono Lake is peppered with Eared Grebes, a duck-like diving bird. Peak populations exceed 700,000 individuals.

AN AVIAN GAS STATION

Mono is a stop of vital importance, not only for grebes and phalaropes, but for other invertebrate-feeding water birds as well. For millenia this lake, like Great Salt Lake in Utah, has served as a "refueling" stop in the arid interior of western North America. The birds pause for days or weeks, fattening on brine shrimp and flies in preparation for the long flights to come. Phalaropes, for instance, lay in stores of fat that almost double their weight and enable them to fly several thousand miles nonstop. The birds cannot depend on Crowley, Tahoe and other western lakes, for they harbor fish and lack Mono's bounty of shrimp and flies. From a bird's perspective it's like undertaking a thousand-mile journey knowing only one or two gas stations have the right kind of fuel.[17]

Birds not only feed at Mono Lake, they change their clothes as well. By mid-summer millions of molted gull, grebe and shorebird feathers are riding the winds and adorning shoreline vegetation. The bountiful food provides the birds with the energy they need to grow new feathers.[18]

A TROUBLED FUTURE

For thousands of years waterbirds have depended on Mono's life-productive waters. If water diversions continue, however, increasing salinity will poison most of the life in the lake. Shrimp and flies will disappear. The birds will return only to find a chemical sump, on whose waters they will starve.*

Why is one of our oldest, most life-productive lakes in mortal danger? Do we have alternatives to Mono's destruction? In the next three chapters we search for answers.

---

*The one exception is the Snowy Plover, which would probably continue to nest in the vicinity of seeps and springs near the shores of the shrunken lake. Unlike the gulls, phalaropes, grebes and other water birds, the plovers are not entirely dependent on the lake's brine shrimp and brine flies, feeding on shore-dwelling insects as well. Owens Dry Lake, for instance, still supports several hundred nesting plovers, but virtually no other water birds.

4

Human History:
kutsavi-eaters to water-seekers

KUZEDIKA PAIUTE

Only 130 years ago, Mono Lake was a blank spot on the white man's map. Nomadic hunters, gatherers and traders dwelt along its shores. They were known to their neighbors as the *Kuzedika,* the *fly-pupae eaters,* for they harvested the pupae and larvae of Mono's brine flies at the end of each summer. "They come from far and near to gather them" wrote William Brewer in 1863. "The worms [pupae] are dried in the sun, the shell rubbed off, when a yellowish kernal remains, like a small grain of rice. This is oily, very nutritious, and not unpleasant to the taste, and under the name *kutsavi* forms a very important article of food. The Indians gave me some. It does not taste bad, and if one were ignorant of its origins, it would make a fine soup."[1]

Using tools fashioned of stone, wood and bone, the Kuzedika Paiute survived in a land that dismayed its first white visitors. They were expert naturalists, intimate by inclination and necessity with every bird, animal and plant. When the snow melted in the mountains, they carried heavily-laden, elegantly-woven willow baskets over the same ancient Mono Pass trail used by present-day backpackers. They traveled as far west as Yosemite Valley, bartering obsidian, pinyon nuts, kutsavi and salt for acorns, manzanita berries and bear skins. In the autumn, when caches were full of pinyon nuts, kutsavi, seeds and rabbit meat, they celebrated with feasts and dance, gambling and games. Storytellers passed the long winter nights with tales of coyote and the creation of Mono Lake.[2]

Or so we must conjecture, for the aboriginal lifeway has been all but obliterated. Only an occasional arrowhead on a lonely beach reminds us of the people who belonged to this land as much as it belonged to them. We, by comparison, are strangers, tourists, newcomers.

MOUNTAIN MEN AND FORTUNE HUNTERS

American and English trappers were the first white men to penetrate the Kuzedika's homeland. As their peers plundered the more accessible Rocky Mountain streams of beaver, mink and other furbearers, men like Jedediah Smith, Peter Ogden and Joseph Walker pushed westwards across the Great Basin towards California and the Pacific. Some were motivated, not just by beaver, but by a sense of manifest destiny. In 1827, when Smith defied Mexican authorities, entered California and became the first white man to cross the Sierra Nevada, he foresaw an American nation stretching "from sea to shining sea." Less than two decades later, Walker was guiding immigrants over trails he had blazed as a trapper. With the gold discovery at Sutter's Mill, the trickle of settlers became a flood of fortune-seekers.[3]

As the routes across the Sierra lay north and south of Mono Lake, the Kuzedika saw few of these early travelers. Their first white visitors may have been Joseph Walker and his trappers. In an account of the 1833 expedition, Zenas Leonard described a lake with "no outlet" and "a great quantity of pumice stone floating on its surface." "Its water," he continued, "is similar to lye . . . [and] admirably calculated to wash clothes without soap."[4] If this was Mono, and not

Kuzedika women, ca. 1900, holding a storage basket; on the ground to her left lie a winnowing tray and a burden basket. The Kuzedika were master basketweavers.

C. Hart Merriam, courtesy Bancroft Library

Carson Lake as some historians believe, Leonard may also be credited as the first in a line of writers (including Mark Twain) to extoll its cleansing qualities.

The Kuzedika undoubtedly heard of the white immigrants crossing the Great Basin. They also heard of the white man's treacherous treatment of neighboring tribes. In 1852 Chief Tenaya's band of Yosemites, pursued by Lieutenant Tredwell Moore and the Second Infantry, fled across Mono Pass to the shore of Mono Lake, where the Kuzedika helped them to escape.[5]

But fate overtook the Kuzedika when Moore and his men discovered gold-bearing quartz near the lake. Leroy Vining was the first of many hard-luck prospectors to set out from the Mother Lode to strike it rich east of the Sierra. Over the years bust followed boom at Lundy, Mammoth, Aurora and many other camps. Biggest of them all was Bodie. In the late 1870s it boasted 15,000 souls, four newspapers, three breweries, dance halls, brothels and other amenities of civilization. Lured by gold, roaring with whiskey and generally soured by hardships and disappointments, the miners plundered the land on which the Kuzedika depended for sustenance.[6]

Three of the white man's activities—lumbering, grazing and hunting—destroyed the Kuzedika's subsistence economy. The mining camps consumed entire forests of pinyon and jeffrey pines for heating, cooking, building and timbering mine shafts. As early as 1860, Leroy Vining gave up prospecting and established a sawmill along the creek that now bears his name. Every cord of wood had to be hauled over 30 miles to the mining districts from the forests south and west of Mono Lake. In 1879 a five-ton steamer was brought from San Francisco for the purpose of ferrying wood to the base of the Bodie grade (on Sundays it was used for picnic excursions to the islands). Two years later the "Rocket" was replaced by a narrow-gauge railroad, constructed by Chinese laborers, which followed Mono's eastern shore from Mono Mills to Bodie. As forests of pinyon fell to the axe, the Kuzedika were deprived of pine nuts, an essential winter staple. The cutting of jeffrey pines drastically reduced the supply of another important food, *piuga,* the fat needle-eating caterpillars of the pandora moth. More than 200,000 sheep, herded up the Owens River from the Mojave Desert and San Joaquin Valley, ruined the meadows where the Kuzedika gathered seeds, bulbs and roots. The sheep also competed with the antelope, bighorn sheep, sage grouse and other animals on which the natives relied for meat and clothing. By the turn of the century, antelope and bighorn had been hunted into oblivion, and the once abundant sage grouse had become scarce. Faced

In the nineteenth century sheep contributed to the downfall of Mono's native people, the Kuzedika Paiute, by grazing meadows to bare earth and competing with native wildlife. "The natural pastures," wrote Russell in 1888, "are now nearly ruined." To this day the lack of sustainable land-use policies allows "hooved locusts" to wreak havoc over much of the Mono Basin.[20]

with starvation, wracked by disease and demoralized by alcohol, the disinherited Kuzedika became the outcasts of a white man's world.

WRITERS AND SETTLERS

Early descriptions of the Mono Lake country reflect the dismay of displaced Easterners in a strange, seemingly hostile land. "A lifeless, hideous, treeless desert," lamented a down-on-his-luck Mark Twain. "The bitter and fatal waters of the lake," reads a newspaper account, "render it literally a dead sea, and all its surroundings—wild, gloomy, forboding—are suggestive of sterility and death."[7] "A strange country," concluded Henry Degroot, ". . . where all nature wears a primitive aspect . . . and where all, except a few valleys and mountain meadows, is a wilderness, silent and vacant, over which the mirage dances and the sandstorm sweeps . . ."[8] To immigrants far from the green, well-watered valleys of the east and midwest, this vast expanse of gray sagebrush, where streams fed a strange salt lake, seemed barren and hostile. Unfortunately the fallacious "dead sea" image colored the perceptions of future generations.

There were, however, some maverick voices. In the summer of 1863, J. Ross Browne, a journalist writing for *Harper's New Monthly Magazine,* followed the rough wagon road from Bodie to Lawrence's Ranch. The Lawrence homestead was one of several pioneer farms along Mono Lake's well-watered, fertile western shore that marketed produce, dairy products and meat in the burgeoning mining camps. Browne spent a night at this "pleasant, home-looking place, with haystacks, wagons, and lowing cattle about the farmyard . . . the house . . . a snug frame shanty, containing three or four rooms, roughly but

Dean Taylor

Tufa kilns west of Cedar Hill. In the 1870s and 1880s, ice-age tufa were calcined in these kilns and found to form an excellent lime.[19]

comfortably furnished."

The Lawrence farm was a pleasant contrast to the bachelor shacks which were Browne's quarters in the mining districts. The Lawrences and their neighbors, unlike the miners, put down roots. They were home-seekers, not fortune-seekers, yet bound economically to the booms and busts of the mining camps. Many of their children continued to till Mono's soil until the hard times of the '30s and big city water interests intervened. A 1908 Mono County promotional tract told of thousands of acres of former "sagebrush land . . . successfully reclaimed by means of irrigation" and yielding handsomely in hay, wheat, barley, potatoes and vegetables.[9] Today the sagebrush has returned, and dry ditches, weathered fence posts and rusted machinery are the only reminders of the dreams of Mono's farmers.

Ross Browne, however, was more than a chronicler of pioneer life. He was one of the first to celebrate the natural landscapes of the American West. In his eyes the "hideous desert" became "one of the finest specimens of scenic graneur." "Vast chasms and rocky canyons," he told his *Harper's* readership, "open out upon the shores of the lake . . . mountain after mountain rolls off in the distance, like the waves of an angry sea . . . mighty potentates of the wilderness . . . in sublime scorn of the puny civilization which encircles their feet. . . ." Unlike the miners and farmers, Browne valued the land, not just for what it could be made to produce, but for its scientific interest and power to uplift the spirit.

In their own way, Mono's pioneers did come to look on the lake as a blessing as well as an oddity. They were thankful that it tempered the climate and extended the growing season. They hunted along its shores, picnicked on its islands and swam in its waters.

In the 1880s Mono Lake became a health spa of sorts. Bath

houses and accommodations were constructed for "invalids and others who may desire to spend a portion of the summer in reach of the healing waters of the lake."[10] Half a century later, lakeside resorts were still luring guests with therapeutic claims. "Mono salts" were bottled and sold as patent medicine.

ROBBING THE GULLS

Wildlife, however, was exploited with pioneer rapacity. Even Mono's gull colonies were robbed of their eggs, which were sold in the mining camps. The Kuzedika had harvested the eggs without depleting the number of gulls. Not so the white man. "It is common practice," wrote Browne, "for the settlers to go over in their boats, and in the course of a few hours gather as many eggs as they can carry home." In later years, the commercial eggers would remain on Negit Island during the entire nesting season. In 1863, "the open spaces between the rocks [were] so thickly covered with eggs that the pedestrian [was] at a loss to find a vacant spot for his foot." Only 20 years later, collectors "commenced looking for eggs but there were very few..."[11] "Gulls," reported a local newspaper, "are becoming very scarce on Mono Lake."[12] In 1916 few still bred on Negit, and only about a thousand pairs still raised young on the lava-covered northern promontory of Paoha Island.[13]

As boom towns became ghost towns and Mono's human population dwindled, Negit's gulls were finally left in peace. Paoha's birds, however, were forced to abandon the island to homesteaders and

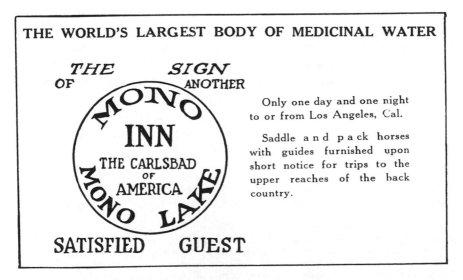

Advertisement for the Mono Inn, ca. 1925.

Michael Dressler

Grant Lake, situated on the June Lake Loop, is a DWP holding reservoir for water diverted from Mono's streams. From here the water flows through a tunnel under the Mono Craters, into the Owens River and on to Los Angeles.

stock. They flourished on Negit, however, increasing to at least 34,000 individuals by 1976 and colonizing the islets to the northeast.

In 1979, however, the Negit Island colony was depleted once again. Not a single gull remained. This time the cause was not the greed of egg-collectors, but the thirst of a distant, ever-growing metropolis.

THE AQUEDUCT BUILDERS

"If we don't get the water," remarked William Mulholland in 1907, "we won't need it."[14] The Irish immigrant and self-taught engineer, who had risen from a ditch-tender to head of the Los Angeles waterworks, was embarking on the most ambitious water project ever undertaken: a 240-mile long aqueduct that would tap the Owens River, its snow-fed tributaries and eventually the next watershed to the north—the streams feeding Mono Lake (Map 5, p. 31). The city had been booming for the past quarter century. Civic leaders, businessmen and land developers realized that the local water supply impeded future growth. Long before actual need they were plotting how to bring more water to the city. Mulholland's ditch was the key, not to survival, but to growth, prosperity and profits.*[15]

The water seekers, like the gold seekers before them, cared nothing for the land. At best they were men like Mulholland, who eschewed personal gain and envisioned a lush, urban paradise for

---

*To promote municipal bond issues to finance the aqueduct, Mulholland and the Los Angeles Times fabricated a drought which never existed. According to Mulholland, average rainfall in Los Angeles between 1895 and 1904 dropped to only six inches per year; in fact, national weather bureau records reveal that precipitation averaged 11.5 inches during this period. Half a century passed before the deception was uncovered.[16]

THE OWENS VALLEY WATER WAR

Cartoon from the *Los Angeles Times*, November 23, 1924, after Owens Valley ranchers "captured" the Alabama Gates and turned the water out of the aqueduct for five days.

During the 1920s, the unquenchable growth of Los Angeles led to a bitter, sometimes violent and devious struggle with Owens Valley residents over water rights.[15] Farmers fought for the land their forebears had wrested from the Paiutes. When conventional methods failed, they vented their frustration by dynamiting the aqueduct 17 times. But the burgeoning, progressive metropolis triumphed over the small, provincial community, leaving a legacy of abandoned houses and barns, "dead trees, weed-grown fields, neglected fences and empty ditches." Los Angeles purchased nearly all the private land, including the towns of Bishop, Big Pine, Independence and Lone Pine. "Purchase of five towns," boasted Chief Engineer H. A. Van Norman, "is . . . unique in the development of water systems throughout the United States."[18] "This was a wonderful valley with a quarter million acres of fruit and alfalfa," lamented Will Rogers, "but Los Angeles had to have more water for its Chamber of Commerce to drink more toasts to its growth, more water to dilute its orange juice . . . so, now this is the valley of desolation."

Thirty thousand people gathered to watch the first Owens-Mono water arrive in Los Angeles on November 13, 1913. Mulholland's speech was to the point: "There it is; take it!"

L. A. Dept. of Water and Power

millions of contented, prosperous citizens. At worst they were men like financier Henry Huntington, newspaper magnate Harrison Gray Otis and others of the "San Fernando syndicate" who, by paying a pittance for "waterless" real estate when the plan for the aqueduct was still a secret, reaped fortunes when the water arrived. Yet the syndicate, for all the corrupt profits it amassed from the municipally-funded aqueduct, did not subvert its primary purpose: urban growth. "There it is, take it," roared Mulholland at the opening ceremonies in 1913. By 1930, the population of Los Angeles had increased from 200,000 to 1,200,000 people, and was still growing. In that year, the city's voters approved another $38 million bond issue to finance the extension of the aqueduct northward from the Owens Valley into the Mono Basin. Unknowingly they had also signed the death warrant for a lake few had heard of, and fewer still had ever visited.

TAPPING INTO MONO

To the men who backed and built the aqueduct, Mono was a worthless, saline "dead sea." If its beauty and wildlife ever crossed their minds, they never spoke of it in public. The project served "the greatest good for the greatest number," and justified, not only the destruction of lakes, but the subjugation of farmers, ranchers and towns (see box: Owens Valley Water War).

The water seekers planned to divert Rush, Lee Vining, Walker and Parker Creeks, four of five major streams feeding Mono Lake, into the Owens River and the Los Angeles Aqueduct via an eleven mile tunnel under the Mono Craters (Map 6, p. 32). In 1931, at the city's behest, Congress withdrew public lands in the Mono Basin "from settlement, location, filing, entry or disposal . . . for the protection of the watershed supplying the City of Los Angeles." The city brought suits to condemn property and water rights, a maneuver calculated to force farmers to sell for lower prices (Map 7, p. 33).[17]

For six years a work force of up to 1,800 men battled steam, boiling water, noxious gasses and cave-ins to drive a tunnel under the Mono Craters. In 1941 the first water was diverted from the Mono Basin into the Owens River, thereby extending the aqueduct system to an intake 338 miles from Los Angeles (farther north than San Francisco). From that moment, Mono Lake began to disappear.

The two Los Angeles aqueducts are marvels of engineering efficiency. The water flows by gravity through tunnels and siphons all the way from Mono to Los Angeles, generating hydroelectric power en route. But it doesn't come for free. At the northern end of the pipe, the "dead sea" is dying.

There rests upon the desert plain what appears to be a wide sheet of burnished metal, so even and brilliant is its surface . . . No prosaic description can portray the grandeur of fifty miles of rugged mountains, rising beyond a placid lake in which each sharply cut peak, each shadowy precipice and each purple gorge is reflected . . .

—Israel C. Russell

Looking west from Mono Lake toward the Sierra Nevada, Mt. Dana (13,053') at top center. Glacier-carved Lee Vining Canyon, with its massive glacial moraines, dominates the center of the photograph. Between the base of the Sierra and Mono's shore, wave-cut terraces mark the beaches of the ice-age lake.   John S. Shelton

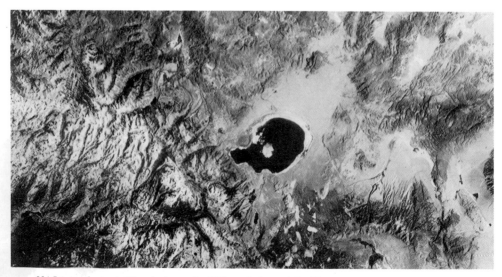

NASA landsat satellite photograph of Mono Lake and the Yosemite region of the Sierra Nevada, August 30, 1977.   United States Geological Survey

Looking east from 55,000 feet across Mono Lake into the parched Great Basin of central
Nevada. Walker Lake, another lake suffering from water diversions, is visible at the upper
left. The photograph was taken July 10, 1968, when Mono stood at 6,388 feet and Negit,
the black island, was separated from the mainland by over a mile of water. Note the ice-age
shorelines encircling the lake, the emerging landbridge between Negit and Black Point and,
at the lower left, the cones and flows of the Mono Craters.   United States Geological Survey

*It is a place stalled in time. For at least a million
years it has reflected the rising wall of the Sierra, itself rising and falling with the advance and retreat
of the mountain glaciers, a geologic heartbeat. Icebergs calved from glaciers have floated silently on
its surface into Nevada, and volcanoes have exploded
from its depths . . .*

—Gray Brechin

Black Point, a volcano that erupted beneath the waters of the ice-age lake.

A fissure on Black Point.

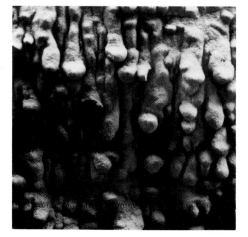

Tufa veneer on Black Point fissure.

A country of wonderful contrasts. Hot deserts
bounded by snow-laden mountains, cinders and
ashes scattered on glacier-polished pavements, frost
and fire working together in the making of beauty.
In the lake are several volcanic islands, which show
that the waters were once mingled with fire . . .
                                            —John Muir

Brett Weston

Pause and you will find broad sand beaches, lapping waves and promontories and islets of strange, spring-formed tufa, like giant towers of cemented cauliflower . . .

—Gray Brechin

A land of stark contrasts, of dramatic gradients, of vast expanses, where even a sense of the passage of time stands graven on the slopes, a superimposed dimension . . .

—David Mason

Philip Hyde

Brett Weston

73

Michael Dressler

A dreamy, spell-like spirit seems to pervade the atmosphere. The smooth, glassy surface of the waters; the upheaved, disrupted volcanic mountains looking down, as it were, into this abyss of their ejection; the illusions of vision and the whitened shores, thickly columned with vesicular lava [tufa] . . . all conspire to impress the mind with the idea of a fictitious scene portrayed by the pencil of an ominipotent hand . . .

—Anonymous, *Sacramento Daily Union*
November 23, 1859

Stephen Johnson

Scanning electron micrograph of calcite tufa crystal, magnified 80 times.

Stephen Johnson, Kenneth Lajoie, Robert Oscarson — U.S.G.S.

Mark Ross

If the day chance to be stormy, we shall see an effect of the wind on the water that but few lakes present. Lake Mono is strongly charged with alkaline salts; when it is agitated by the wind, the waves break into foam which gathers along the leeward shore in a band many yards wide and sometimes several feet thick. Sheets of this tenacious froth are caught up by the wind and driven inland through the desert shrubs in fluffy masses that look like ball of cotton . . .

—Israel C. Russell

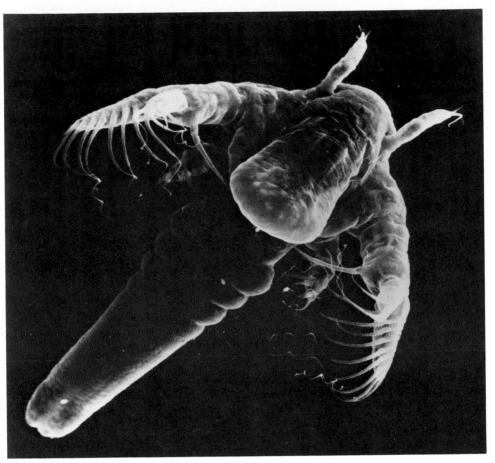

Brine shrimp nauplius, 48 hours old, magnified 75 times.
Daniel Gunther

The shores hum with brine flies and, though the lake is too alkaline to support fish, you will see it swarming with transparent bodies of brine shrimp. Heated by the sun, this briny soup spawns simple life in phenomenal abundance. . . .

—Gray Brechin

Snowy Plover and chick.   Ian Tait

Wilson's Phalarope.

Joseph R. Jehl, Jr.

Galen Rowell

*Few sights in nature are lovelier than the airy calli-
graphy of phalaropes en masse, darting, banking and
diving by the hundreds in perfect unison over the
still water. Joined by avocets, gulls, grebes and other
waterfowl, the lake literally teems with millions of
birds at the height of the season, bringing the sounds
of the sea to the continent's dry interior . . .*

—Gray Brechin

Stephen Johnson

The next time you pass by Mono, check the lake's living pulse. Is its surface peppered with birds? Can you hear the cries of gulls and grebes? What will you see and hear in years to come?

1962: The tops of two tufa towers barely
visible above Mono's surface.

1968: The same tufa towers entirely
exposed.

1978: The towers high and dry. Since diversions began, Mono Lake has fallen 44 vertical
feet and doubled in salinity.

Michael Beaucage

Michael Dressler

Raw and incongruous at first, you must give it time.
Moreover, treat it with the respect you would give a
very old, very wise person . . .

—Gray Brechin

5

Turning Paradise Into Alkali

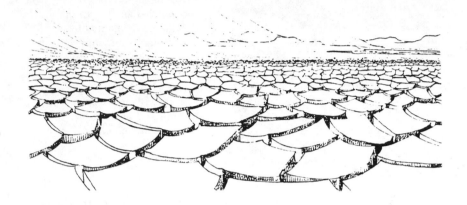

Early in April of 1979, explosions shattered the stillness of Mono Lake. In a last-ditch attempt to save the gull colonies, the California National Guard tried to blast a moat around Negit Island. Their efforts failed to deter coyotes, which invaded the island, routed the birds and preyed on their eggs and chicks. In 1980, despite the erection of a "predator-proof" fence, the gulls refused to return. Fortunately about three-fourths crowded onto small islets northeast of Negit and west of Paoha. If diversions are not curtailed, however, these islets too will soon be connected to the mainland. By 1990 even Paoha Island will be a peninsula.

Homeless gulls are only the beginning of an ecological nightmare. Since diversions began, Mono Lake has fallen 45 vertical feet. Its volume has been halved and 15,000 acres of alkali-encrusted shoreline have been exposed to the sun and wind. At present diversion rates, the lake is projected to drop another 50 feet before it stabilizes at one-third its natural surface area and less than one-fifth its natural volume (Map 12).[1]

As Mono Lake shrinks, its carbonates, sulfates, chlorides and other solutes become ever more concentrated. Salinity has already doubled.* Unless diversions are reduced, salinity will triple by the

---

Salinity and *salt buildup* as used in this chapter refer to increasing concentrations of all solutes in Mono Lake's water, not just table salt (sodium chloride).

Jim Stroup

"Saving Gulls Is A Blast," headline a newspaper account. In early spring of 1978 and again in 1979, the California National Guard, in cooperation with Fish and Game, attempted to dynamite a channel between Negit Island and the mainland. But they couldn't keep pace with the receding lake. In 1979, coyotes invaded the island, routing the gulls and preying on their eggs and chicks.

turn of the century and quadruple by the year 2015 (Figure 9). Mono's shrimp, flies, algae and birds can thrive in saline, alkaline water up to a critical concentration, but not beyond. Long before the lake stabilizes, if it ever does, that point will be passed and Mono will become a chemical sump.

OWENS DRY LAKE

It has happened before. One hundred twenty miles to the south, between Los Angeles and Mono Lake, lie a hundred square miles of glaring white alkali. Only old-timers recall the broad expanse of water that reflected Mt. Whitney and its neighboring Sierran summits in the days before the Owens River was shunted into the Los Angeles Aqueduct. Looking across the parched, barren depression that once was Owens Lake, clouds of dust rising from its surface, it is difficult to imagine steamboats plying its waters or millions of birds feasting along its shores. By 1928, sixteen years after the completion of the aqueduct, Owens Lake had turned into dust.

"Owens Lake," wrote Israel Russell a century ago, "is in many ways the homologue of Mono." He was comparing their similar geology, water chemistry and ecology. Now, as Gray Brechin says so aptly, Owens has become "the image of Mono's future, the dusty sump of a desiccated valley." Mono, like Owens, has been hooked up to the aqueduct.

Owens is not the only Great Basic lake that has been drunk dry by thirsty humans. Thousands of aquatic birds used to gather on Nevada's Humboldt, Carson and Winnemucca Lakes, Utah's Sevier Lake and California's Honey Lake. Today these bodies of water are ephemeral alkali ruins, their tributary waters shunted to farms and cities (see Map 2, p. 27). The remnants of Walker and Pyramid Lakes, like Mono, are slowly being strangled by water diversions. Even Great Salt Lake is threatened. Mono embodies the crisis of vanishing wetlands and wildlife throughout the American west.

The Los Angeles Aqueduct under construction, ca. 1910. The Mono Basin extension was completed in 1941.

Los Angeles Department of Water and Power

Owens is one of many Great Basin Lakes that have already been drunk dry by thirsty humans. Sixteen years after the Owens River was shunted into the Los Angeles Aqueduct, Owens Lake had turned into dust. Will Mono Lake be next?

PROJECTING THE FUTURE SIZE OF MONO LAKE

The future size of Mono Lake will depend on how much water is exported from its watershed in years to come. At present diversion rates, it is projected to stabilize at an elevation of about 6,223 feet—50 feet below its present level—toward the middle of the next century. If diversions are increased and augmented by groundwater pumping, however, it will probably dry up completely.

Hydrologists project the effect of water exports on Mono's size by modeling the lake's water balance. The model is conceptually simple: CHANGE IN VOLUME OF LAKE = STREAM INFLOW + GROUNDWATER INFLOW + SURFACE PRECIPITATION INFLOW — EVAPORATIVE OUTFLOW (see Figure 2, p. 30). Prior to water diversions, inflow tended to balance outflow, keeping the lake more or less stable. In recent years diversions have reduced stream and groundwater inflows by approximately 60 percent, causing the lake to shrink. As it shrinks, its surface area contracts and evaporative outflow decreases. Eventually, if water exports are not increased, inflow will again balance outflow, and the lake will stabilize at a smaller size.

Exactly what size is uncertain, for inflows and outflow can only be estimated. Precipitation and evaporation have not been accurately measured; groundwater inflow has not been measured at all. Still, assuming the continuation of present climatic conditions, the projections that follow are probably in the ballpark.[1]

Projected Stabilization Level	Diversions (acre-ft/yr)	Surface Area (acres)	Volume (acre-ft)	Comments
6,410 feet	0	53,500	4,050,000	no diversions
6,388 feet	15,000	49,000	2,800,000	Task Force recommendation; Negit landbridge submerged
6,385 feet	18,000	48,000	2,750,000	elevation required to preserve Negit Island*
6,375 feet	35,000	42,000	2,350,000	Negit Island connected to mainland
6,373 feet	40,000	40,000	2,300,000	1981 elevation
6,369 feet	46,000	38,000	2,100,000	elevation required to preserve Paoha Island*
6,359 feet	60,000	32,000	1,700,000	Paoha Island connected to mainland
6,323 feet	100,000	22,500	780,000	present diversions

*with 10-foot buffer against natural fluctuations in lake level

THE DEADLY SALT BUILDUP

If a man were dying of thirst, we would not deprive him of water while trying to decide how long he could manage to survive. Yet, so long as diversions continue, Mono Lake is being treated in precisely this fashion.

The impact of salt buildup can be sudden and devastating. For three years, biologists watched a saline, alkaline lake in Africa increase in salinity without detecting any dramatic ecological changes. Then, in less than four weeks, Lake Nakuru's food chain collapsed. Without warning most of its algae perished and thousands of birds disappeared.[2] Eventually, if diversions are not curtailed, Mono will suffer Nakuru's fate—perhaps this year, perhaps two decades from now. Whenever it happens, the collapse will be swift and quite possibly irreversible.

Recent studies confirm this prognosis. In 1976 University of California biology students assayed the survival rates of brine shrimp and brine fly larvae in Mono Lake water concentrated in increments to approximately three times present salinity. In water of approximately twice present salinity, the effects were traumatic. Most of the shrimp died from osmotic (salt) stress. The fly larvae coiled up,

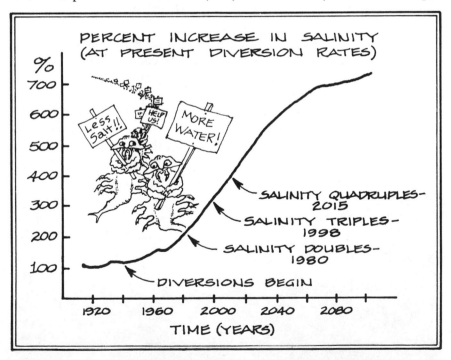

Figure 9. Mono Lake's salinity has already doubled. Unless diversions are curtailed, salinity will triple by the turn of the century and quadruple by the year 2015, poisoning the lake's birds, shrimp and other living inhabitants.

HOW MUCH LONGER CAN MONO LAKE SURVIVE?

Studies indicate that Mono Lake's brine shrimp and brine fly larvae may survive to twice present salinity—until the year 2000 at current diversions rates. That is, if their eggs still hatch, if their young mature, if algae survive . . .

Increasing salinity could jeopardize Mono's ecosystem in ways that have not been studied, perhaps not even foreseen. For example, a smaller, shallower lake will warm to higher temperatures in summer. The warmer, saltier water will hold less dissolved oxygen—which may impact shrimp and fly larvae. At higher water temperatures, the shrimp and flies may be more vulnerable to salt stress.

As Mono Lake shrinks in size, its water will also increase in density. Brine shrimp, flies, algae and birds (and humans, too) will find it easier to float. But this could restrict the shrimp to surface waters, greatly depleting their numbers. Their eggs might no longer sink to the bottom, reducing the hatch.[6]

Unless diversions are curtailed, Mono may become a biologically depauperate sump even before the turn of the century. Each year diversions continue increases the risk of the lake's demise.

clumped together and reduced physiological activities to a minimum. They survived, but no longer grew or developed.[3]

Nor is it likely that Mono's shrimp and flies will somehow adapt to highly concentrated lakewater. The diverse chemistry sets the odds against them, for they would have to cope, not just with chlorides, but with sulfates, carbonates and other solutes as well.

Moreover the salt buildup will affect, not just shrimp and fly larvae, but algae and birds as well. At Lake Nakuru, the algae suddenly died off. If the same happens at Mono, the shrimp and flies, and in turn the birds, will starve. Every part of the living community

C. Hart Merriam, courtesy Bancroft Library

Mono Lake in 1900, showing the nearly two miles of water separating Negit (black) island from the mainland.

ARE BIRDS AS NUMEROUS AS THEY USED TO BE?

Photograph by C. Hart Merriam, ca. 1900, showing brine flies darkening Mono's shore. Such dense concentrations have not been observed since the 1950s.

Since water diversions began in 1941, Mono Lake's salinity has doubled. Has this affected birds and the shrimp and flies on which they feed?

Undoubtedly yes, but to what extent may never be known. Nobody studied the Mono Lake ecosystem before diversions began. In the early 1960s, when David Mason first surveyed Mono's shrimp and algae, salinity had already increased nearly 50 percent. By 1976, when comprehensive bird counts were initiated, it had almost doubled.[7] Qualitative, anecdotal impressions are the only information from earlier years. Still some disturbing trends are obvious.

Ducks were almost certainly more numerous. An 1852 newspaper article, the first mention of Mono Lake in print, speaks of "wild ducks and gulls, in abundance . . ."[8] In 1865 J. Ross Browne described a "gunning expedition" as "nothing short of wholesale slaughter . . . 20 or 30 teal duck at a shot is nothing unusual . . . sportsmen find it a laborious job to carry home their game." Ducks from Mono Lake were sold house to house in Bridgeport.[9] Older residents, who recall taking two to three hundred a day and salting them down, lament the decline since diversions began.[10] Increasing salinity and lack of fresh water are plausible causes, for most ducks, unlike gulls, phalaropes and grebes, lack well-developed salt glands.

Brine fly populations have likely declined as well. Most historic accounts reinforce Mark Twain's description of "a belt of flies one hundred miles long . . . an inch deep and six feet wide." A photograph taken by C. Hart Merriam around the turn of the century shows brine flies (and possibly their larvae or pupae) blackening the shore for as far as the eye can see.[11] The annual Paiute harvest depended on this abundance. When numbers of flies dwindled during the 1950s, the harvest ceased.[12] Recent studies at Great Salt Lake correlate salinity and brine fly populations—the greater the salt, the fewer the flies.[13]

Algae, brine shrimp, shorebirds, grebes and gulls still seem to be healthy despite the doubling of salinity. But are they as abundant as they used to be? Nobody can say.

Michael Dressler

A few years ago, the Negit Island landbridge was covered with water. Is this the Mono Lake our children will inherit?

is intimately linked to every other. If the base of the food chain fails, the rest inevitably follow.

SALT-STRESSED BIRDS

Increasing salinity is a serious threat to Mono's birdlife. As birds feed, they swallow saline lakewater along with shrimp and flies. No bird yet studied, even those with specialized salt-excreting glands, could survive for long on Mono's brine. To prevent salts from concentrating to toxic levels within their bodies, gulls, shorebirds, ducks and other water birds gather at freshwater streams and springs to drink, bathe and generally cleanse their systems of excess salts.*

If salinity continues to increase, birds will have to resort to fresh water more and more frequently. Eventually they will have insufficient time for feeding. Water diversions compound the burden by desiccating the streams and springs on which the birds depend.[4]

The gull chicks seem especially vulnerable. Marooned on Mono's island nurseries, they never taste fresh water until they fledge.

ALKALI SMOG

In place of flocks of birds, our children will inherit clouds of dust. Already the pollution has violated both state and federal 24-hour ambient air quality standards. During Mono's frequent windstorms, billowing alkali erupts from 17,000 acres of exposed lakebottom, rises thousands of feet in the air and travels hundreds of miles before being deposited on vegetation and wildlife. An airline

---

*Mono's Eared Grebes, however, do not visit these freshwater sources. Are they able to cope with the lake's salinity? Do they drink from fresh, lakebottom springs?

pilot has mistaken the dust for an active volcano. At present diversion rates, at least another 5,000 acres will be laid bare by the turn of the century and air pollution will continue to increase.

At Owens Lake the dust has already reached disastrous proportions. It fills thousands of square miles with a dense chemical smog that creeps into the canyons of the adjacent Sierra Nevada and Inyo Mountains. It is affecting pine trees and afflicting local residents with respiratory ailments.

Because of its chemical composition, the Mono dust bodes even worse. It contains ten times the sulfates of Owens dust, as well as

Looking north across the landbridge toward Negit Island on a calm day.

The same view on a windy day. Alkali dust blowing off the exposed lakebed pollutes the air and endangers human health far from Mono's shores.

other substances suspected to be toxic to plants, animals and humans. The minute size of the dust particles aggravates the health hazard, for they can be drawn deep into the sensitive regions of the lower lungs.[5]

At the very least Mono's dust will ruin the view, plague visitors and residents, and jeopardize the local, tourist-based economy—for who will want to vacation near a dustbowl? At worst it could spread a swath of desolation over hundreds of square miles—killing trees, shrubs and grasses, sickening humans and wildlife and leaving the land barely habitable.

WHAT WILL BE LOST?

What will we lose if we trade Mono Lake for alkali dust?

1. A wildlife resource and unique ecosystem.

Mono's millions of birds are an integral part of a highly productive, unique community attuned to an ancient alkaline lake unlike any other on our planet. An entire ecosystem, not just a species, is threatened with extinction.

More is at stake than one lake's wildlife, Mono is a link in a flyway that stretches across the Americas. From British Columbia to Baja California gulls depart from beaches, towns and fields to rear their young on Mono's islands. Grebes and ducks born in Canada feed at the lake en route to Mexico. So do sandpipers and phalaropes migrating from the tundra to South America. Most of these birds have nowhere else to go. Too many links in the flyway have already dried to dust.

2. A scientific resource.

Because of its relatively simple, yet highly productive biological community, Mono is an ideal natural laboratory for ecological research. Such studies enlarge our understanding of the more complex ecosystems on which we directly depend.

3. A place of national park stature.

Mono is America's most extraordinary body of water, a lake which people, not just birds, treasure and enjoy. Every year tens of thousands of visitors walk its beaches, boat and swim in its waters, marvel at its volcanoes and tufa spires, or just enjoy its pristine, spacious setting. What they find cannot be measured monetarily or easily put into words. Gray Brechin calls the lake "an awesome place . . . where the grand processions make you acutely aware of being alive on the planct."

courtesy of Robert Curry

1880s: The geologist Israel Russell paddles among the tufa towers west of Black Point.

Viki Lang

1981: Where's the lake? It's a mud-slogging mile away.

1949: Flowery meadows extend to Mono Lake's shores. Negit Island (right background) is separated from the mainland by almost two miles of water.

Viki Lang

1981: A bathtub ring of white alkali and viscous mud encircles the lake. Negit Island is connected to the mainland, and predators have routed its nesting gulls.

6

Common-sense Water Use Can Save Mono Lake

Stephen Johnson

Carrying buckets, canteens and bottles of water, several hundred marchers filed down the highway and across the alkali towards Mono's shore. The buckets, filled above the Lee Vining Creek diversion dam, were emptied into the lake. Signs were waved at passing motorists: "Don't Owensize Mono," "DWP—Waste Not Want Not," "Mono Lake Belongs To Itself."

The annual "bucket brigade" reflects the growing concern over Mono's plight. In response to this concern, the California Department of Water Resources convened an Interagency Mono Lake Task Force in December, 1978. Representatives from Water Resources, Fish and Game, Bureau of Land Management, Forest Service, Fish and Wildlife Service, Mono County and Los Angeles Department of Water and Power were charged with developing "a plan of action to preserve and protect the natural resources of the Mono Basin, considering economic and social factors." One year later, after sixteen meetings, three public workshops and three public hearings, the Task Force released its recommendations: curtail diversions and raise the lake.

THE TASK FORCE COMPROMISE

The Task Force Plan is a compromise. It would not end diversions or restore Mono Lake to pristine conditions. It would raise the lake to its 1970 elevation of 6,388 feet—high enough to safeguard gull rookeries and reduce, but not eliminate, dust pollution. Until the lake attains that elevation, the plan would cut diversions by an average of 85,000 acre-feet per year.*

But how would Los Angeles replace the water? While 85,000 acre-feet is only 0.2 percent (1/500th) of the total consumed by Californians annually, it still amounts to 4 percent of urban Southern California's consumption and 14 percent of Los Angeles' consumption (Figure 10). Tapping alternative sources would not only be expensive, it would export Mono's ills to other watersheds.

Fortunately the Task Force proposed a solution that does not hold San Francisco Bay, the Eel River, Owens Valley or any other watershed ransom for Mono's life. The plan ultimately requires no replacement water supplies, no change in water-use habits, saves en-

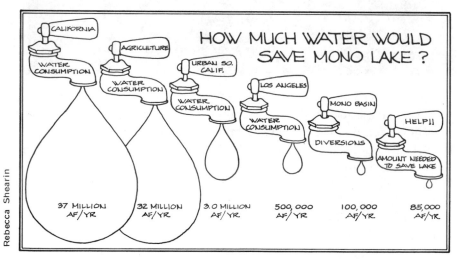

Figure 10. By reducing diversions by 85,000 acre-feet per year, Mono Lake would return to a healthy elevation of 6,388 feet. This amounts to 1/500th of the water currently consumed by Californians in an average year.

---

*An *acre-foot* is enough water to flood one acre of land one foot deep.

"Brick as art object . . . toilet tank as gallery." In 1979 Los Angeles artist Deborah Small crafted 50 porcelain Mono Lake bricks designed to displace water in recipients' toilet tanks. She sent them to public officials with the power to influence Mono's destiny. Simple, common-sense water conservation methods could save Mono Lake many times over.

ergy, and costs Los Angeles residents 54¢ per person per year—about a penny per week. In five to seven years, it would reduce Los Angeles' yearly thirst by more than the 85,000 acre-feet needed by the lake. How? Through water conservation and wastewater reclamation.

Ninety-five percent of all household water ends up in the sewer. The Task Force Plan would cut this waste with low-flush toilets, water-saving toilet devices, low-flow showerheads and flow restrictors. Estimated savings in Los Angeles: 41,000 acre-feet annually.

California is one of the few arid lands on earth that uses water once, then dumps it into the sea. The Task Force calls for reclamation of so-called wastewater for uses in irrigation, industry and groundwater recharge. Estimated savings in Los Angeles: 56,000 acre-feet annually.

Contrary to its critics, who raise the specter of "strict water rationing," the Task Force Plan relies entirely on proven, mechanical conservation methods that require no change at all in habits. It does not even prohibit hosing down driveways, flooding gutters and other profligate water uses.*

---

*The Task Force estimates that elimination of "conspicuous waste" could save another 36,200 acre-feet of water annually in Los Angeles.

The Task Force Plan would save energy, too. When water is conserved, the energy to treat, distribute and heat that water is also conserved. Energy savings from the Task Force water conservation program would amount to the energy equivalent of 650,000 barrels of oil per year. This energy savings would exceed the loss in hydroelectric generation along the aqueduct by about 200,000 barrels of oil annually.[1]

But the Los Angeles Department of Water and Power (DWP) has fought the Task Force Plan. DWP claims that conservation and reclamation are "unrealistic," that "there is little potential for achieving the necessary additional conservation without regular water rationing," that the cost "in terms of water, energy and dollars is clearly unreasonable." Citing the most expensive alternative sources, DWP reckons the costs at $10 million annually for water and $15 million annually for power, i.e., about $7 per Los Angeles resident per year—14 times the Task Force estimate of 54¢.

The difference hinges on the viability of conservation and reclamation. According to the Task Force, we can slake our thirst on less water, spare Mono Lake, and save dollars and energy too. According to DWP, we can barely conserve another drop. Whom do we believe?

THE TASK FORCE RECOMMENDATIONS

In December, 1979, the Interagency Task Force on Mono Lake recommended a plan to protect Mono Lake (Plan P). Its key points are as follows:

1. Los Angeles would be required to reduce water diversions from 100,000 to 15,000 acre-feet per year until Mono Lake returned to an elevation of 6,388 feet. During extreme drought conditions, however, diversions could be increased.

2. Los Angeles residents would be required to reduce water consumption by 6 percent through the installation of flush-reducing toilet dams, low-flow shower heads and similar devices.

3. Los Angeles would be required to reclaim wastewater for use in irrigation, industry and groundwater recharge.

By 1986, according to state studies, conservation and reclamation would reduce Los Angeles water consumption by more than the 85,000 acre-feet per year needed by the lake. Until this time, the cost of replacement water would be shared by the state (36 percent), the City of Los Angeles (36 percent) and the federal government (28 percent). The costs of expanding conservation and reclamation, and of replacing the loss in hydroelectric power (one percent of L.A.'s supply), would be borne by Los Angeles alone. After 1986, however, energy savings (about 650,000 barrels of oil per year) would more than compensate costs to the city.

THE LESSON OF THE CALIFORNIA DROUGHT

During 1976 and 1977, Californians weathered the worst drought in the state's history. With rainfall a fraction of normal and reservoirs reduced to puddles, people had to conserve. In 1977 urban water consumption dropped by 20 percent, saving 434,000 acre-feet state-wide. The San Francisco Bay Area conserved 32 percent, while Marin County and some Sierran foothill communities conserved over 50 percent.[2] More water was saved than anyone, especially the water purveyors, thought possible. The drought exposed our water-wasteful ways, and taught us we could thrive on much less.

The people of Los Angeles conserved 16 percent (97,000 acre-feet), more than enough to save Mono Lake. No lawns withered, no swimming pools were drained and virtually no one complained of the hardships of sweeping leaves off driveways or watering lawns in the evenings.

By comparison the Task Force Plan is modest. According to California Water Resources, common sense conservation could save not just 41,000 but at least 140,000 acre-feet of water per year by the turn of the century.[3] Reclamation could recycle not just 56,000 but at least 100,000 acre-feet annually. In the City of Los Angeles alone![4]

If every California community adopted the Task Force Plan, the savings would exceed 500,000 acre-feet per year. Millions more could be conserved by California agriculture. If we all conserved, farmers

California's surplus water is no longer in our streams and ground-water basins. It's in our drains and gutters being wasted through thoughtless consumption. If we all conserved, farmers as well as urban dwellers, we could cut California's thirst by at least three million acre-feet annually . . . enough to save Mono Lake 15 times over.

Michael Dressler

as well as urban dwellers, San Franciscans as well as Angelenos, we could cut California's thirst by at least three million acre-feet annually . . . enough to save Mono Lake 35 times over.

A WET YEAR/DRY YEAR APPROACH

Still there are times when thirsty humans do need a little of Mono's water. During the 1976–77 drought, for instance. For this reason the Task Force Plan provides for increasing diversions "during any period of extreme drought conditions," i.e., when alternative supplies are truly unavailable.[5] The lake would not begrudge this if

SOUTHERN CALIFORNIA HAS ADEQUATE WATER
(without destroying Mono Lake, San Francisco Bay, North Coast Rivers, etc.)

Projected Water Supply and Demand in Urban Southern California*

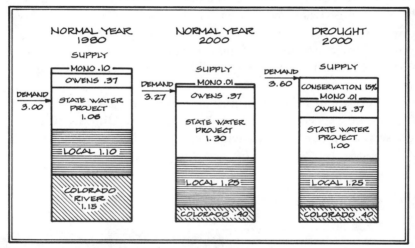

*Within service area of the Metropolitan Water District of Southern California, i.e., most cities from Ventura to the Mexican border and east to San Bernardino, including Los Angeles.

Urban Southern California does not require any additional water supplies to meet future needs at least through the turn of the century. The present supply exceeds demand by about 800,000 acre-feet per year. Even assuming a 30 percent increase in population, the loss of over half the Colorado River entitlement, no peripheral canal and the implementation of the Task Force Plan, supply in the year 2000 would still exceed demand in years of average and above average precipitation. Fifteen percent conservation, the state goal for all California communities, could remedy the shortfall during extended droughts.[7]

we let it rise when the rains returned.

   But DWP rejects this "wet year/dry year" compromise. They
want it all, every year, regardless of need. For example, the 1970s
closed with the wettest three year period in Los Angeles history. If
diversions had been curtailed Mono Lake would have risen about five
vertical feet. Negit would still be an island. The lake's health would
not be imperiled. But, although inexpensive alternative supplies were
available, DWP took every drop the aqueduct system could handle.
As a consequence, the lake fell from a January 1978 elevation of
6,375 feet to an early 1981 elevation of 6,373 feet.

GREED, NOT NEED

   Why isn't DWP more generous? Because Mono Basin water is
inexpensive—about one-third the price of other imported supplies.
It flows by gravity all the way to Los Angeles. In contrast water from
the Colorado River and the State Water Project is pumped over mountain ranges, greatly increasing its cost.

   Although Los Angeles taxpayers have paid over $350 million to
maintain rights to over 600,000 acre-feet of Colorado River and State
Project water, DWP uses as little as possible from these sources (see
table). Instead, to maximize profits, they squeeze all they can from the
Owens Valley and Mono Basin. Since 1970, Mono-Owens have furnished nearly 80 percent of the Los Angeles municipal supply. Mono's
contribution has increased to nearly 17 percent of the total. Conversely average purchases from other sources have declined from
about 150,000 to only 25,000 acre-feet per year.[6]

LOS ANGELES WATER SUPPLY AND DEMAND
(in acre-feet per year)[6]

	1980	1990	2000
Projected Water Supplies			
Local Sources			
Groundwater	102,500	102,500	102,500
Reclaimed Water	56,000	218,400	235,200
Imported Sources			
Owens Valley-Mono Basin	470,600	470,600	470,600
Colorado River	348,200	137,500	133,200
Northern California	305,500	566,200	555,300
Total	1,282,800	1,495,200	1,496,800
Projected Water Demand			
With Water Conservation	553,000	530,000	498,000
Without Water Conservation	602,000	636,000	654,000

OWENS VALLEY GROUNDWATER PUMPING

In 1970, with the completion of a second Los Angeles Aqueduct, the "Owens Valley water war" flared again. This time the conflict was not over surface water, but over groundwater. To fill the second aqueduct, DWP not only doubled Mono Basin diversions, they also increased ground-water pumping in the Owens Valley beyond all expectations. Dismayed by desiccated springs, dying vegetation and a dramatic increase in the frequency and intensity of dust storms, the people of Inyo County went to court, charging DWP with failing to prepare an environmental impact statement. They've been there ever since.

Inyo County has won battles, but not the war. In 1973 the court forced DWP to prepare an EIR. The resultant document, however, was a travesty. The court, ruling in 1977, declared the EIR legally inadequate and chastized DWP's misrepresentation of the pumping as "serious," "wishful" and "egregious." A second draft is still being challenged. Meanwhile pumping continues.[8] *ALSO REJECTED OCT 1981*

In November, 1980, the conflict took a new turn. Inyo County voters passed an ordinance to regulate groundwater pumping. The ordinance gives Inyo an effective weapon, provided they can weather legal challenges. DWP has already filed suit. With county budgets strained, Inyo can barely afford another prolonged lawsuit. But neither can it afford the browning of the Owens Valley.

MONO LAKE AND THE PUBLIC TRUST

In April of 1979, the National Audubon Society, Los Angeles Audubon Society, Friends of the Earth, Mono Lake Committee and four Mono Basin landowners filed a lawsuit against the Los Angeles Department of Water and Power. The suit alleges that the unrestricted diversion of Mono Lake's tributary streams violates the *public trust*—a legal doctrine that dates back to Roman times. The seed of this doctrine is contained in the sixth century codes of Justinian, which state that "by the laws of nature these things are common to mankind—the air, running water, the sea and consequently the shores of the sea." As traditionally applied, the public trust has protected public navigation, commerce and fishing in all navigable waters, including lakes. In recent years the California Supreme Court has extended the public trust to preservation of tidelands as "ecological units for scientific study, as open space, and as environments which provide food and habitat for marine life, and which favorably affect the scenery and climate of the area" (Marks vs. Whitney 1971).

The Audubon lawsuit, if successful, would force DWP to reduce its diversions to a level that does not interfere with the public's use and enjoyment of Mono Lake. Because of the complexity of the case, it has yet to come to trial.

WATER CONSERVATION BEGINS AT HOME

Conserving water is a simple, fundamental thing to learn, like brushing one's teeth or looking before crossing the road. It's something kindergarten kids can comprehend and practice, and it's something they, along with all of us, must do. Here are some suggestions:

- Five to seven gallons gush through the typical flush toilet at every flushing. The simplest way to conserve is to flush less often. You can easily save even more by placing water-filled plastic containers, weighted down with pebbles, into your toilet tank. Two one-quart soap or bleach bottles will displace one-half gallon of water and save that much at every flushing.

- About 30 percent of interior water is consumed by showering and bathing. Just taking shorter showers, washing hands in the basin instead of under a running faucet, turning off the tap while brushing teeth, and so forth can save many gallons a day. These savings can be greatly augmented through the installation of flow restrictors, aerator or efficient water-saving heads on showers and sink faucets.

- You can conserve water outside your house by watering the yard only as needed and by landscaping with geraniums, honeysuckle, ceanothus and other water-eschewing plants.

For further home conservation advice, contact your local utility. They should have free pamphlets and other materials on water-saving techniques.[9]

DWP is playing a shell game. By increasing Mono-Owens diversions, they free an equivalent amount of Colorado River and State Project water. This water allows more of rural southern California to be subdivided, especially Orange and San Diego Counties. Mono is being sacrificed, not to meet present needs, but to fuel future urban sprawl.

During 1980, DWP stifled all attempts to implement the Task Force recommendations. At hearings before the California legislature, they claimed that:

> There is no scientific evidence whatsoever that the use by the City of Los Angeles of Mono Lake water is highly detrimental to Mono Lake . . .
>
> The reliction of the lake does not destroy its beauty . . .
>
> Mono Lake has *never* sustained any water or lake-related recreation; no swimming! no boating! no water skiing! no fishing . . . no nothing . . .

Unfortunately such distortions carry weight in Sacramento, where

"No nothing" speedboat races on Mono Lake, circa 1935.

the credibility and clout of a powerful water agency eclipse that of scientists, water policy reformers and a small rural county. Despite the Task Force, Mono Lake continues to die.

WATERSHED HOUSEKEEPING

"While the gulls are important in their own right," says California Resources Secretary Huey P. Johnson, "they also are an important symbol of the conflict between constant demand for increased use of resources and the growing awareness that there are limits to those resources."[7] When will those limits be recognized? Will Mono Lake, like Owens before it, be sacrificed to the seemingly insatiable water demands of an ever-increasing population? To be followed by San Francisco Bay, the Eel River, the Yukon, and on and on until the last of our wetlands have vanished? Until the gull and brine shrimp follow California's state animal, the Grizzly Bear, into extinction? Until we tip the balance of nature against our children?

Mono's plight indicts the wasteful ways of all of us. Angelenos consume no more than most Americans. Wherever we live we have been profligate in our use of water and other precious resources. Wherever we live, there are Mono Lakes at the other ends of our taps.

The choice is ours. We can still leave our children a living Mono Lake. But we must support water conservation and reclamation as the life-giving alternatives to ever more dams, aqueducts and wasteful water projects that sicken our environment and mortgage our future. We must become watershed housekeepers, responsive to the needs of the land from which we draw our sustenance and health.

"Water and power conservation . . . a way of life" proclaims the stationery of the Los Angeles Department of Water and Power. By sparing Mono Lake, DWP could transform this slogan into a living example for the rest of the country and the rest of the earth.

Epilogue

by Gray Brechin

If there are place spirits, Mono has one of the strongest I have ever encountered. It's easy to personify the lake; I sometimes wonder what it thinks as its millions of years of existence come to an abrupt end. I have thought of Mono as an old friend for so many years that it now looks to me like a prone patient being bled to death on an operating table, and I wonder if that great reservoir of experience dreams back to the ground-breakings and upthrust of the Sierra which gave it birth, to the icebergs and volcanic formations which have reflected on its surface in the recent past. Morbidly I wonder if it will stink when its prodigious life finally expires on the bone-white lakebed.

Whether Mono Lake has a consciousness will remain one of its mysteries. But Mono endows its friends with awareness, for we have all had to learn from it. Mono has taught us to see the world anew, to accept and perceive beauties we had been unaware of, and to ask questions whose answers may be far from simple or comfortable. On the solitude of its beaches, at dawn and at dusk, we have learned to listen and to watch and to live quietly with ourselves. But mostly, we have learned to live with other beings which we cannot use but whose mere presence enhances our daily existence.

Mono doesn't ask simple questions. It demands an examination of the inner and outer worlds which constitute human awareness. And that is why it is the best kind of friend, and that is why we cannot let it die.

Words of Thanks

This guidebook has been brewing since Sally Judy, David Winkler, Mark Ross and myself, wrenched by Mono's plight, formed the Mono Lake Committee in the spring of 1978. To these friends of many years I am indebted for unwavering support, occasional criticism and high spirits. In particular, Sally's love and encouragement brought this booklet to fruition.

The board of the Mono Lake Committee, in particular Anne Foster, Ellen Hardebeck, Grace de Laet and Bob Langbauer, never lost faith in the worth of this project. Our underpaid, dedicated staff, Tom Cassidy, Emily Hart, Sally Judy, Dean Taylor and Kathleen Teare, freed my time for writing.

The following friends read the manuscript, corrected embarrassing inaccuracies and proffered invaluable advice: Dr. Sarane Bowen, Gray Brechin, Sara Burnaby, Tom Cassidy, Gayle L. Dana, David B. Herbst, Joseph R. Jehl, Jr., Sally Judy, Dr. Kenneth Lajoie, Petra Lenz, Dr. John M. Melack, Doris Sloan, Genny Smith, Scott Stine, Kathleen Teare, Peter Vorster and David Winkler. To Genny Smith, Sara Burnaby and Sally Judy I am especially indebted for weeding redundancies and rhetoric from the manuscript.

The following artists, photographers and organizations allowed work to be reproduced without compensation: Craig Aurness, The Bancroft Library, Michael Beaucage, Michael Dressler, Liane Enkelis, Frasher's Photography, Keith Hansen, Tony Hertz, Philip Hyde, Joseph R. Jehl, Jr., Sharon Johnson, Stephen Johnson, Joyce Jonte, Kenneth Lajoie, Viki Lang, Martin Litton, Los Angeles Department of Water and Power, Eben McMillan, National Geographic Society, Mark Ross, Becky Shearin, John S. Shelton, Jim Stroup, Dennis Studer, Ian Tait, Dean Taylor, United States Geological Survey and Brett Weston. Stephen Johnson, inveterate Monophile and curator of the *At Mono Lake* exhibition, arranged for the reproduction of many photographs. Kenneth Lajoie donated the USGS photographs. Viki Lang spent endless hours in the darkroom transferring color transparencies to black-and-white. James Carew designed the cover.

In addition to everyone listed above, it gives me pleasure to thank the following new and old friends for "resonating" with me at crucial times during these Mono Lake years and contributing thereby to the genesis of this guidebook: Bob Barnes, Ted Beedy, David Brower, Elliot Burch, Steve Cunha, Bob Curry, Jean Dale, Mary DeDecker, David DeSante, Brett Engstrom, Howard Ferguson, Joyce Hall, Barbara Horton, Early Human, Huey Johnson, Joanne Kerbavaz, Jeanine Koshear, Corliss Kristensen, Susanne Luther, Palmer Madden, George S. Peyton, Jr., Phil Pister, Michael Ross, Stuart Schulz, Bev Stevenson, Rich Stallcup, George Stroud, Tim Such, Evan Sugden, Meryl Sundove, Chris Swarth, Dan Taylor and Stephanie Zeiler.

To the people of Lee Vining I am grateful for friendship and encouragement. In particular I thank Lily Mathieu, Wes Johnson, Harriet Hess and Don Banta for useful historical information.

I owe more to my parents than anyone else, for they nourished my love of nature and hopes for a friendlier, more peaceful world.

Finally I thank Ma Nature for Mono Lake, a beautiful planet and all our brother and sister living beings.

—D.G.
Mono Lake, Spring, 1981

Sources

Listed are the primary sources of information consulted in the preparation of this booklet. Abbreviations have been used for the following key references:

DWP = Los Angeles Department of Water and Power

DWR = California Department of Water Resources

Ecological Study = Winkler, David W., ed., 1977, *An Ecological Study of Mono Lake,* Univ. Calif. Davis Inst. Ecology Publ. 12; reprinted with an update by the Mono Lake Committee (1980)

Lajoie = Lajoie, Kenneth R., 1968, *Quaternary Stratigraphy and Geologic History of Mono Basin,* Ph.D. Thesis, Univ. Calif.

Mason = Mason, David T., 1967, *Limnology of Mono Lake, California,* Univ. Calif. Publ. Zoology 83

Russell = Russell, Israel C., 1889, *The Quaternary History of the Mono Valley, California,* U.S. Geol. Survey 8th Annual Report: 267–394

Task Force Report = California Department of Water Resources, Southern District, 1979, *Report of the Interagency Task Force on Mono Lake*

The J. Ross Browne quotes are from "A Trip to Bodie Bluff and the Dead Sea of the West," *Harper's New Monthly Magazine* (1865) 31:411–419; Mark Twain's are from *Roughing It,* Chapters 38 and 39; Grey Brechin's are from "Elegy for a Dying Lake," *San Francisco Examiner,* October 1, 1978.

Chapter 1

1. Ecological Study, p. 61.
2. Russell, pp. 278–9.
3. *Homer Mining Index,* 10 May 1884.
4. For an etymology of *Mono,* see: Merriam, C. Hart, 1955, *Studies of California Indians,* Univ. of Calif. Press, pp. 164–8. Contrary to Ella Cain (*Early History of Mono County,* Fearon Publ, p. 3), *Mono* is not a Paiute word for *beautiful*—it is not a Paiute word at all.
5. Russell, p. 320 ff.

Chapter 2

1. For a history of Great Basin explorations, see: Cline, Gloria G., 1963, *Exploring the Great Basin,* Univ. Oklahoma Press.
2. For a masterful overview, see: Russell, pp. 269–86. The Muir quote is from *My First Summer in the Sierra.*
3. Russell, p. 287; Mason, p. 6; Lajoie, p. 26; Kenneth Lajoie, pers. comm.; for source of salinity percentages, see note 6.
4. Colcord, R. K., 1928, Reminiscences of Life in Territorial Nevada, *Calif. Historical Quarterly* 7:112.
5. For a survey of terminal lakes of the world, see: Greer, Deon C., ed., 1977, *Deseric Terminal Lakes,* Utah State Univ. For a discussion of saline lake chemistry, see: Eugster, Hans P. and Lawrence A. Hardie, 1978, Saline Lakes, in *Lakes: Chemistry, Geology, Physics,* Springer Verlag, pp. 237–93.
6. Data on Mono Lake's present salinity, chemical composition and pH derive from: Herbst, David B., 1980, *Ecological Physiology of the Larval Brine Fly,* Master's Thesis, Oregon State Univ., p. 8; Task Force Report, p. 17. The Task Force, however, errs in omitting bicarbonates, hence their figure for salinity (8.4%) is about one percent low. The figure in the Ecological Study (10.5%; p. 43) is also in error. For salinity prior to diversions, see: Russell, pp. 292–6; Task Force Report, p. 16. Source on other waters:

107

Lake Tahoe Research Group, pers. comm.; Greer, D. C. ed., 1977, *Desertic Terminal Lakes,* p. 27.

7. The quotes are borrowed from (respectively) Gray Brechin, J. Ross Browne and Kenneth Brower (*Country Journal,* August, 1980).

8. Some scientists, including Russell, have thought that algae were critical to tufa formation; see for example: Scholl, D. W. and W. H. Taft, 1964, Algae, Contributors to the Formation of Calcareous Tufa at Mono Lake, *Jour. Sedimentary Petrology* 34:309-19. Recent investigators, however, accord algae a subordinate role. See: Dunn, J. R., 1953, The Origin of the Deposits of Tufa in Mono Lake, *Journal of Sedimentary Petrology* 23:18-23; Cloud, Preston and K. R. Lajoie, 1980, Calcite-Impregnated Defluidization Structures in Littoral Sands of Mono Lake, *Science* 210:1009-12.

9. Mason, pp. 14-26; Lajoie, pp. 30-32; Loeffler, Robert M., Ecological Study, pp. 15-16.

10. Loeffler, R. M., Ecological Study, pp. 15-16.

11. The 1857 elevation given by S. T. Harding, 6,376', is drastically in error (Harding, 1965, *Recent Variations in the Water Supply of the Great Basin,* Water Resources Archive Series Report 16:1511-170). Harding's fallacious figure was perpetrated in many subsequent publications, including the Ecological Study (pp. 11-13). For an exhaustive analysis of Mono Lake's 1857 elevation and subsequent fluctuations, see: Stine, Scott, 1981, *Reinterpretation of the 1857 Surface Elevation of Mono Lake,* Water Resources Archive Series Report: in press.

12. The "geologic heartbeat" image was borrowed from Gray Brechin.

13. Lajoie, pp. 34-46; Gilbert, C. M., M. N. Christensen, Y. Al-Rawi and K. R. Lajoie, 1969, Volcanism and Structural History of Mono Basin, *Geol. Soc. Amer. Memoir* 116; Kenneth Lajoie, pers. comm.

14. Axtell, L., 1972, Mono Lake Geothermal Wells Abandoned, *Calif. Geology* 25(3):66-7.

15. For a review of climate and vegetation change in the Great Basin, see: Tidwell, William D., S. R. Rushforth and D. Simper, 1972, Evolution of Floras, *Intermountain Flora,* v. 1, Hafner Publ. Co., pp. 19-39.

16. Russell, pp. 299-320; Lajoie, pp. 12-28.

17. Kenneth Lajoie, pers. comm.

18. Hill, Mary, 1975, *Geology of the Sierra Nevada,* Univ. Calif. Press, p. 116.

19. Bailey, R. A., G. B. Dalrymple and M. L. Lanphere, 1976, Volcanism, Structure and Geochronology of the Long Valley Caldera, *Jour. Geophys. Research* 81:725-44.

20. Russell, pp. 378-89.

21. Christensen, M. N. and C. M. Gilbert, 1964, Basaltic Cone Suggests Constructional Origin of Some Guyots, *Science* 143:240-2; Lajoie, pp. 147-58.

22. Russell, pp. 371-7; Lajoie, pp. 141-7; age of islands—Scott Stine, pers. comm.

23. Scholl, D. W., R. Von Huene, P. St.-Armand and J. Ridlon, 1967, Age and Origin of Topography Beneath Mono Lake, *Geol. Soc. Amer. Bull.* 78: 596; Kenneth Lajoie, pers. comm.

24. For a summary of the conflicting theories, see: Stewart, J. H., 1976, Basin-Range Structure in Western North America, *Geol. Soc. Amer. Memoir* 152:22 ff.

25. Lajoie, pp. 110-11; Scott Stine, pers. comm.

26. Scott Stine, pers. comm.; the date on the stumps was published in: *Radiocarbon* 4:112.

27. Russell, p. 286 ff.; Scholl, D. W., R. Vone Huene, P. St.-Armand and J. Ridlon, 1967, *Age and Origin of Topography Beneath Mono Lake, Geol. Soc. Amer. Bull.* 78:583-99.

28. Lajoie

Chapter 3

1. Calif. Dept. of Fish and Game, Bishop office, files.

2. Lenz, Petra H., 1980, Ecology of an Alkali-adapted Variety of *Artemia* from Mono Lake, in *The Brine Shrimp Artemia,* vol. 2, Universa Press, Wetteren, Belgium.

3. Herbst, David B., Ecological Study, p. 86.

4. For additional information on algae and primary productivity, see: Mason, pp. 78-95; Lovejoy, Connie and Gayle Dana, Ecological Study, pp. 42-57.

5. Dana, G. and David B. Herbst, Ecological Study, pp. 57-62; Lenz, Petra H., ibid.

6. Mason, pp. 89-95; John Melack, pers. comm.

7. Aldrich, J. M., 1912, The Biology of Some Western Species of the Dipterous Genus Ephydra, *N.Y. Entomological Assoc.* 20:85-93; Herbst, David B. and Gayle Dana, Ecological Study, pp. 62, 73-86.

8. Ecological Study, p. 62 (tentatively identified as *Culicoides varipennis*).
9. Calif. Dept. of Fish and Game, Bishop office, files.
10. Gaines, David, 1977, *Birds of the Yosemite Sierra,* Cal-Syl Press; Winkler, D. W., C. P. Weigen, F. B. Engstrom and S. E. Burch, Ecological Study, pp. 88–113; *Amer. Birds* 32:1051; David Winkler, pers. comm.
11. A re-analysis of census data by University of California biologist David Winkler has revised the breeding gull population estimates given in the Ecological Study (pp. 89 ff.). The 1976–78 population is now believed to have numbered about 51,200 breeding adults. In 1979, when predators routed the Negit Island colonies, the population dropped to about 21,000. In 1980, with gulls crowding onto the small islets, it increased to about 40,200 (David Winkler, pers. comm.).
12. For distribution, see: Woodbury, A. M. and H. Knight, 1951, Results of the Pacific Gull Color-banding Project, *Condor* 53:57–77. For biology see: Johnston, D. W., 1956, The Annual Reproductive Cycle of the California Gull, *Condor* 58:134–62, 206–21; Winkler, D. W. et al., Ecological Study, pp. 100–113.
13. Morgan, Dale L., 1947, *The Great Salt Lake,* Univ. New Mexico Press, pp. 213–15.
14. Point Reyes Bird Observatory, Gary Page, pers. comm.
15. For a summary of phalarope biology and migrations, see: Palmer, Ralph S., 1967, *The Shorebirds of North America,* Viking Press, pp. 264–7. Additional refinements from Joseph Jehl, Jr. and David Winkler, pers. comm.
16. For estimates of phalarope and grebe populations in 1976, see: Ecological Study, pp. 95–100. Phalarope numbers were significantly lower in 1980 (Joseph Jehl, Jr., pers. comm.).
17. The "gas station" analogy was suggested by Sally Judy.
18. Joseph Jehl, Jr., pers. comm.
19. Sarane Bowen, Gayle Dana, Petra F. Lenz, pers. comm. For a review of brine shrimp taxonomy, see: S. T. Bowen, M. L. Davis, S. R. Fenster and G. A. Lindwall, 1980, Sibling Species of *Artemia,* in *The Brine Shrimp Artemia,* Vol. 1, Universa Press.

Chapter 4

1. Brewer, William H., 1966, *Up and Down California in 1860–1864* (journals edited by Francis P. Farquhar), Univ. Calif. Press, p. 417.
2. For an excellent, overall description of Kuzedika culture, see: Smith, Genny S., 1976, *Mammoth Lakes Sierra,* Genny Smith Books, Palo Alto, pp. 128–31. For more in-depth accounts, see: Merriam, C. Hart, 1955, *Studies of California Indians,* Univ. Calif. Press, pp. 71–6; Davis, Emma Lou, 1965, *An Ethnography of the Kuzedika Paiute of Mono Lake,* Univ. Utah Anthropological Papers 75:1–55.
3. For an account of the explorations of the trappers, see: Farquhar, F. P., 1965, *History of the Sierra Nevada,* Univ. Calif. Press, pp. 23–39.
4. Quaife, M. M., ed., 1934, *Narrative of the Adventures of Zenus Leonard,* R. R. Donnelly and Sons.
5. Farquhar, op. cit., pp. 78–9.
6. The voluminous literature on Bodie and the other Mono mining camps suffers from an emphasis on shootings, lynchings and sensationalism. Ella M. Cain's *The Story of Bodie* (1956, Fearon Publishers, San Francisco) is representative. A sober, comprehensive history of early Mono County has yet to be written. For the bare bones of such a history, see: Chappell, M., 1947, Early History of Mono County, *Calif. Historical Soc. Quarterly* 26:233–48; Russell, C. P., 1928, Early Mining Excitements East of Yosemite, *Sierra Club Bull.* 13:40–53; Cain, Ella M., 1961, *The Story of Early Mono County,* Fearon Publishers, San Francisco.
7. *Sacramento Daily Union,* Nov. 19, 1868.
8. Degroot, H., 1860, *Sketches of the Washoe Silver Mines,* Hutchings and Rosenfield, San Francisco.
9. McIntosh, F. W., ed., 1908, *Mono County, California: The Land of Promise for the Man of Industry,* Mono County Board of Supervisors.
10. *Homer Mining Index,* May 10, 1884.
11. Denton, S. W., arranged by V. Denton, 1949, *Pages from a Naturalist's Diary,* Alexander Printing Co., Boston, pp. 20–21.
12. *Homer Mining Index,* June 23, 1883. A similar entry on June 3, 1882 reads: "the crop of gull eggs on the island in Mono Lake is small this season; the depredations on the

birds' nests have probably caused them to seek some safer spot to rear their young."

13. Dixon, J., Unpublished Field Notes of May 27–28 and July 3, 1916, Museum of Vertebrate Zoology, Univ. of Calif., Berkeley.
14. Quoted in: Ostrom, Vincent, 1953, *Water and Politics,* The Hayes Foundation, Los Angeles.
15. For a terse, excellent review of the Los Angeles Aqueduct and the Owens Valley "water war," see: Smith, Genny S., 1978, *Deepest Valley,* William Kaufman Inc., Los Altos, pp. 192–7. For more in-depth accounts, see: Nadeau, Remi, 1974, *The Water Seekers,* Peregrine Smith, Inc., Santa Barbara; Kahrl, William C., 1976, The Politics of California Water: Owens Valley and the Los Angeles Aqueduct 1900–1927, *Calif. Historical Soc. Quart.* 55:2–25, 98–120. For engineering details, see: City of Los Angeles, Dept. Public Service, 1916, *Complete Report on Construction of the Los Angeles Aqueduct;* Van Norman, H. A., 1936, The Mono Basin Project, *Civil Engineering* 6:306–8.
16. Kahrl, W. C., op. cit., p. 8.
17. DWP, 1974, *Los Angeles Water Rights in the Mono Bason and the Impact of the Department's Operations on Mono Lake.*
18. Van Norman, H. A., 1930, $38,000,000 Will Provide Needed Water for Los Angeles, *Pacific Municipalities* 44:202–3.
19. Russell, p. 314.
20. Russell, p. 278.

Chapter 5

1. DWP; Loeffler, Robert M., *Ecological Study,* pp. 23–38; Kenneth Lajoie, pers. comm.
2. Melack, John M., 1979, Temporal Variability of Phytoplankton in Tropical Lakes, *Oecologia* 44:4–5; John Melack, pers. comm.
3. The 1976 studies are reported in: Herbst, David B. and *Ecological Study,* pp. 63–9. Subsequent research has corroborated the original findings; see: Herbst and Dana, 1980, Environmental Physiology of Salt Tolerance in an Alkaline Salt Lake Population of *Artemia* from Mono Lake, *The Brine Shrimp Artemia,* Vol. 2, Universa Press, Wetteren, Belgium, pp. 157–67; Herbst, 1980, *Ecological Physiology of the Larval Brine Fly,* Master's Thesis, Oregon State University.
4. Winkler, D. W. et al., Ecological Study, pp. 111–13.
5. Reinking, R. F., Larry A. Mathews and Pierre St.-Armand, 1975, *Dust Storms Due to the Desiccation of Owens Lake,* International Conference on Environmental Sensing and Assessment, Las Vegas, Nev.; Barone, John B., Bruce H. Kusko, Lowell L. Ashbaugh and Thomas A. Cahill, 1979, *A Study of Ambient Aerosols in the Owens Valley Area,* Final Report to the California Air Resources Board, Contract No. AU-178-30; Fryxell, Charles L., 1980, *Dust Cloud Impact—An Overview of the Impact of the Water Gathering Activities of the City of Los Angeles on the Air Quality in the Great Basin Valleys Air Basin,* Great Basin Unified Air Pollution Control District; Task Force Report, pp. 22, 73–4; Charles Fryxell, pers. comm.
6. Dana, Gayle et al., Ecological Study, pp. 57, 61.
7. Mason's *Limnology of Mono Lake* (1967), the first study of Mono's biology, did not examine the lake's birdlife. During the summer of 1976, a group of university students supported by the National Science Foundation investigated the geology, hydrology, limnology, botany, entomology and ornithology of Mono Lake, conducted the first systematic bird censuses, and discussed the impact of continued water export on the lake's ecology; the Ecological Study was the result.
8. *Alta California,* October 3, 1852.
9. Cain, Ella, 1961, *The Story of Early Mono County,* p. 46.
10. Conversations with Lee Vining residents Lily Mathieu and Wesley Johnson.
11. Merriam, C. Hart, 1955, *Studies of California Indians,* Univ. Calif. Press.
12. Davis, Emma Lou, 1965, *Ethnography of the Kuzedika Paiute,* Utah Anthropological Paper 75:33.
13. Collins, N. C., 1980, Population Ecology of *Ephydra cinerea, Hydrobiologia:* in press.

Chapter 6

1. Task Force Report, pp. 47–9. To obtain the 650,000 barrels of oil/year figure, it is necessary to convert the natural gas savings from therms into barrels of oil and to add the electrical energy savings. Hydroelectric generation loss resulting from the reduction

of Mono Basin diversions amounts to the equivalent of 435,000 barrels of oil per year—
one percent of Los Angeles municipal electrical demand.

2. DWR, 1978, *The 1976–1977 California Drought: A Review.*
3. DWR, So. District, 1977, *Effect of Conservation on South District Urban Water Demand for 1980, 1990 and 2000.* These projections have been verified in pilot studies in Ventura and San Diego Counties; see: DWR, So. District, 1979. *A Follow-up Survey of Households Which Participated in the San Diego Pilot Water Conservation Program* and *22 Months Later the Oak Park Retrofit Program Still a Success.*
4. Orange and Los Angeles Counties, 1978, *Water Reuse Study.*
5. Task Force Report, pp. 45–6.
6. For Los Angeles water supply information, see: So. Calif. Assoc. of Governments, 1977, *Compilation and Analysis of Water System Data—City of Los Angeles.* For conservation potential, see: DWR, So. District, 1977, *Effect of Conservation on South District Urban Water Demand.*
7. For urban Southern California water supply and demand projections, see: Metropolitan Water District of Southern California, 1979, *Water Supply and Demand Data.*
8. For an excellent presentation of the viewpoints of both sides, see: Smith, Genny, ed., 1978, *Deepest Valley,* William Kaufman, Inc., pp. 201–27.
9. The first paragraph is borrowed from Dan Taylor, *Mono Lake Committee Newsletter* 2(4):8.

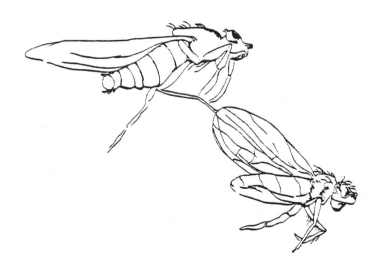

Joyce Jonte

Index

Aeolian Buttes, 39
Algae, 14, 42-7, 87-9
  role in tufa formation, 22

Bacteria, 44
Black Point, 6, 40, 70
Birds, 14, 42-3, 48-57, 78-9, 89-90
Bishop tuff, 36, 39
Bodie, 4, 60
Bodie Hills, 40
Brewer, William, 58
Brine fly, *see:* fly, brine
Brine shrimp, *see:* shrimp, brine
Browne, J. Ross, 44, 63, 89

Cedar Hill, 37
Cowtrack Mountain, 40

Diatoms, 41
Dust, alkali, 4, 90-92
DWP, *see:* Los Angeles, Department of Water
  and Power

Fly, brine, 14, 42-4, 47-8, 87-9
  use as food by Paiutes, 14, 58
Fremont, John C., 16

Glaciers, 10, 12, 68
Glass mountain, 4
Grant Lake Reservoir, 11, 64
Great Basin, 4, 16, 27
  dry lakes, 27, 85
  ice-age lakes, 27, 37
Great Salt Lake, 19-20, 47
Grebe, Eared, 46, 49-50, 56-7, 90
Gull, California, 4, 14, 49-53, 63-4, 83-4,
  90
  routed from Negit Island, 83
  taking of eggs, 63

Hawthorne Highway, 4

Ice-age, *see:* Mono Lake, ice-age
Indians, *see:* Paiutes

Lake Nakuru, 87
Lake Tahoe, 19-20, 44
Lee Vining, 19
Lee Vining Diversion Dam, 10, 95
Leonard, Zenas, 59-60
Long Valley caldera, 39
Los Angeles Aqueduct, 10-11, 32, 64-6, 85
Los Angeles Department of Water and
  Power, 5, 66, 95, 98, 101-4
  opposition to Task Force Plan, 98, 101,
  103-4
  purchase of Mono Basin farms, 5, 66

Merriam, C. Hart, 89
Mono Basin, climate, 23-5
  early descriptions, 61-2
  farms, 5, 61-2
  first whites, 59-61
  geological history, 26, 35-7
  land ownership, 5, 33
  mining booms, 4, 60
Mono Craters, 11-12, 17, 39-40, 66
Mono Inn, 6-7
Mono Lake, age, 36
  birdwatching, 3
  boating, 3
  camping, 3
  fluctuations in level, 28-9, 38
  future size, 86
  geographical features, 17-18, 68-9
  health spa, 62-3
  ice-age, 2, 4, 30, 37-9, 68-9
  impact of water diversions, 11, 14, 34,
  81, 83-94
  Interagency Task Force, 95, 100, 101-6
  lawsuit, 102
  salinity and alkalinity, 13-14, 18-21, 76,
  107
  swimming, 3, 15
  thermal stratification, 46-7
  water balance, 24-6
Mono Lake County Park, 5-6
Mono Lake ecosystem, absence of fish, 42
  adaptation to salinity, 44
  diversity and productivity, 42-4
  food web, 42-3
  impact of increasing salinity, 14, 57, 83-4,
  88-90
  importance to birds, 14, 49, 57, 92
  scientific value, 92
Mono Lake Marina, 7
Mono Lake Vista Point, 1-4
Muir, John, 17, 71
Mulholland, William, 64-5

Navy Beach, 15
Negit Island, 2, 7-8, 23, 41, 63-4, 83, 88,
  90

Ocean, 19-20
Owens Dry Lake, 84-5, 91
Owens Valley, groundwater pumping, 102
  water war, 65

Paiute, Kuzedika, 13, 14, 58-61, 63
Panum Crater, 12-13
Paoha Island, 7-8, 23, 39, 41
  homesteaders, 8-9
Phalaropes, 42, 49-50, 53-6
Plover, Snowy, 50, 53

Poconip, 24
Public trust doctrine, 102

Rattlesnake Gulch, 4
Rush Creek, 11
Russell, Israel C, 7-8, 22, 37-8, 67, 84, 93

Shrimp, brine, 14, 42-7, 77, 87-5
  harvest, 7-8
Smith, Jedediah, 57-8
South Tufa, 13-14

Task Force, *see:* Mono Lake, Interagency
  Task Force
Thinolite, 4-5, 23
Tioga Lodge, 7

Tufa, 4-6, 21-3, 62, 74-5, 108
  ice-age, 4-5, 22
  sand, 15, 22
Twain, Mark, 18, 25, 42, 45, 61

Vining, Leroy, 9, 60
Volcanoes, 7-8, 11-12, 39-41

Walker, Joseph, 59-60
Water conservation and reclamation, 97-
  100, 103-4
Water diversions, Mono Basin, 10-11, 32, 66
  hydroelectric generation, 66, 98
Water supply, California, 96
  Los Angeles, 96, 101
  Southern California, 96, 100
White Mountains, 1

Snowy Plover and chick.
Keith Hansen

I am not normally a birdwatcher, yet I know that a great deal of animation and grace will pass from the world if Mono dies. . . . You watch the passage of moon, sun and stars over the knife-edged horizons, the rose dawn projected on the granite screen of the Sierra and the jagged shadows of evening reach across the lake into Nevada and the sky beyond. You watch the birds in their arrivals, departures and intricate ceremonies and stalking grace, and you take comfort and joy from such order and cyclical permanence. It is hard to watch this spectacle crumble to dust . . .

—Gray Brechin